Key Stage 3 English
Literacy Strategy Workbooks

These 3 books have been written specifically to follow the Literacy Strategy for KS3.

Each page has questions covering a Teaching Objective from the Literacy Strategy. Tips have also been included for some of the more difficult questions.

And there's even the odd ever-so-nearly entertaining bit, just to help keep you awake.

Contents

Section One — Spelling

Section Two — Vocabulary

Section Three — Sentences and Paragraphs

Section Four — Different Types of Non-Fiction

Section Five — Different Varieties of English

Contents

Section Six — Research and Study Skills

Section Seven — Author's Craft

Section Eight — Literary Texts

Section Nine — Essay Skills

Section Ten — Writing Fiction

Section Eleven — Writing Information

Section Twelve — Writing to Persuade

Section Thirteen — Critical Writing

Published by Coordination Group Publications Ltd.

Contributors:
Adrian Burke
Alex Cherian
Taissa Csáky
Mary Drayton
Dominic Hall
Lorraine Hill
Shona McIntosh
Allison Palin
Simon Parker
Glenn Rogers
Alison Sagrott
Julie Schofield
Claire Thompson
Jenny Watson
Elizabeth Wheatley
Chrissy Williams

Also Starring:
a small goat, on backing vocals

With Thanks to:
Rosemary Cartwright for the proofreading.

ISBN 1 84146 136 9

Groovy website: www.cgpbooks.co.uk

Printed by Elanders Hindson, Newcastle upon Tyne.

Choosing the Right Vowel

Q1 **Write out this sentence, underlining all the long vowels and circling all the short ones:**

The fat man broke the chain on his bike on the way to the quiz show.

Q2 *All the words in the box have the same long **a** sound, but they are spelt differently.*

a) Make three lists of these words. There should be one list for each different spelling of the long **a** sound.

rain	spray	play	sail	place
stay	snail	make	fail	today
brake	snake	main	clay	same

b) What are the three different ways of spelling the long **a** sound?

Q3 Write out these sentences, filling in the gaps:

a) He fell over in the p.....ground and cut his knee.
b) You shouldn't go to the reptile house if you don't like sn....s.
c) He didn't br..... quickly enough and hit the car in front.
d) It always r.....s on sports d..... .
e) We have the s..... thing for tea every night.
f) I'm going to m..... something out of c..... in art.
g) She goes to her class like a sn..... and leaves like a runaway tr..... .
h) Can you ex........ to me why you need to leave the classroom ag..... ?

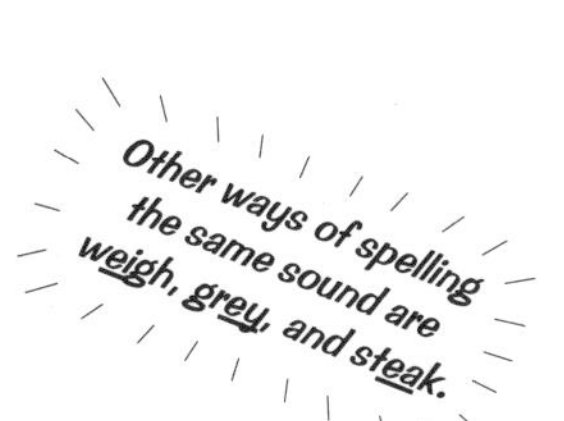

Q4 Practise spelling these two long vowel sounds — **ea/ee** and **ight/ite**. Write out these sentences correctly:

a) We've practised hard so we can beet that teem.
b) I'm supposed to switch off my lite at 9.30.
c) Ellie is the same hite as Sarah.
d) Vegetarians don't eet meet.
e) He tried to cheet in the exam but was caught.
f) She took a big bight out of my sandwich and now I don't want it.

Short and long — just like my grandad's memory...

Some vowels take a lo-o-o-ng ti-i-i-me to sa-a-a-y and some are just a quick snap of the lip. But you already knew that... That's just normal speech. You don't need to be told that. Er... sorry.

Spotting the Right Spelling

Q1 Copy out these words and put a circle round the vowel that you don't say (or don't say as much) — the unstressed part of the word:

e.g. bus(i)ness

interested	vegetable	fattening
totally	necessary	definitely
easily	Wednesday	difference

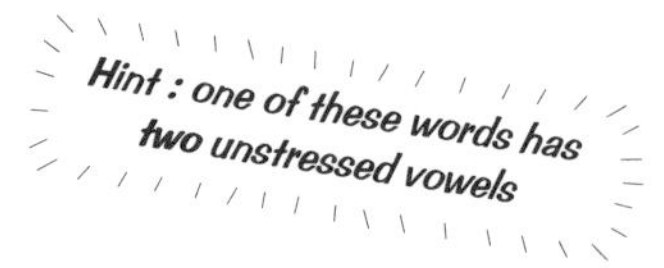

Q2 Write out these sentences, choosing **er**, **en** or **ar** to fill in the gaps:

a) If the ball goes over the bound..y, you score a four.
b) Their band practice was deaf..ing.
c) She desp..ately wanted a part in the play.
d) He always felt like giggling in the libr..y.
e) Prim..y school seems a long time ago.
f) Some of the things my sister wears are quite fright..ing.
g) I always get sep..ated from my friends because we talk too much.
h) They said it was volunt..y but I don't remember putting up my hand.

Q3 Copy out the examples below. Rewrite them so they are all spelt correctly.

e.g. He preferred bating to bowling.
should be — *He preferred batting to bowling.*

Short vowel sound = double consonant
Long vowel sound = single consonant

a) His thumb just fited in the plughole, but then it was traped.
b) She was so excited she began hoping up and down on the spot.
c) They hopped to find homes for all the baby rabits before the next lot arrived.
d) They thought that hootting the horn would be a good way to hurry their mum up.
e) When they saw the look on her face, they wished they'd stoped.
f) He fell when he sawwed off the branch he was siting on.
g) I felt as if everyone was starring at me.
h) The staring role in the play will be given to the best singer.

Q4 a) Write out this sentence, circling the soft **c**s and underlining the hard ones:

The celebrity cuddled his cat in the centre of the cemetery.

b) Write out the words beginning with a soft **c**:

circle	car	coat	city	circus
care	ceiling	cub	cellar	call
century	cot	cut	cement	cinder

c) What letters make it soft?

Sometimes the same can happen in the middle of a word, like December. A y can also make the c soft in words like cylinder and cymbals.

Plurals

*Plural means more than one — one friend, lots of friends. For most plurals, just add **-s**.*

Q1 Change the words in brackets to plurals to match the rest of the sentence.
*If a word ends in **ch, tch, s, sh, ss, x** or **z**, you add **-es**, not **-s**.*

a) The (bench) were piled so high they nearly fell on Mr Stewart.
b) We'll be in trouble when my sister sees we've eaten all her (sweet).
c) She always rushes everywhere as if she's being chased by a pack of mad (dog).
d) The police need (witness) for the accident outside the shop.
e) I haven't done my homework because the computer has lost all my (file).
f) Why do two (bus) come at once when there haven't been any for an hour?
g) I have to practise three (waltz) on my violin before I'm allowed out.
h) There are a lot of (fox) living in towns these days.

*Words ending in **y***
*If there's a vowel in front of the **y**, as in boy, you just add **-s**.*
*If there's a consonant in front of the **y**, as in curry, you change the **y** to **-ies** — curries.*

Q2 Divide these words into two lists — one that should end in **-s** and one that should end in **-ies**.

baby monkey ruby story subway key spray sky fly valley

Choose three from each list. Make them into plurals by adding **-s** or **-ies**. Use each one to write a sentence.

Q3 There are some mistakes in the plural endings in following passage. Find the mistakes, and rewrite the passage using the correct plurals.

My favourite animal is a donkey. One of the reason I like donkies is that they have great long eares. Their favourite hobbys are eating, sleeping and playing frisbee. The older ones don't play frisbee though — instead they go to buy meat and vegetablies, and make gravy. I used to have lots of fieldes to keep donkies in, but, ever since it rained cats and dogies last Tuesday, I have to keep them all in boxs. I don't think they like it much in there, but I've promised to give them all pet puppys if they promise not to behave.

The plural of cake means getting really fat...

Step-by-step guide to plurals: 1) Stop and think. 2) Look at the letters carefully. 3) Add what you think is the right ending. 4) Check the word looks right. 5) If it doesn't, head for the dictionary...

Plurals

Words ending in vowels
*The good news is there are some rules... If a word ends in **o**, you usually just add **-s**.*
*The bad news is that if there's a consonant in front of the **o**, watch out.*
*Sometimes you add **-es**. Learn these words and impress everyone by getting them right:*

echoes heroes potatoes tomatoes

Q1 Work out the plurals of the words below, then copy out the sentences and use the plurals to fill the gaps.

tomato kilo stiletto radio echo hero video potato stereo

a) Any shop that sells televisions will probably sell .... , ... and .... too.
b) The avalanche sent .... all down the valley.
c) My dog weighs about six ....
d) I don't know which of the super......... is my favourite.
e) If I'm going to sell vegetables, I'll have to be able to spell .... and ....
f) If someone wearing .... steps on your foot, it hurts a lot.

*A number of words that end in **-f** or **-fe** have to change to **-ves** when they become plurals.*
*They are — **calf, half, knife, leaf, life, loaf, shelf, thief, wife, wolf, yourself**.*

*Some words end in **f** but you just add **-s**, like chief, cliff and spoof.*
The good news words are dwarf, handkerchief, hoof and scarf — you can use either.

Q2 Write out this story, correcting all the mistakes in it:

The chieves wifes had started putting their loafs up on high shelfs and covering them with handkerchiefs because the wolfs kept behaving like thiefs and stealing them. This frightened the calfs in the hills and they kept running towards the clifves in panic. This was threatening the lifes of the chieves' people. It also left marks of hooves in the loafs, so something had to be done.

"We'll have to get the dwarves in," said the chief.

The dwarfs sharpened their knifes, wrapped themselfs in thick scarfs and hid in the leafs to wait for the wolfs. The wolfs, who were not stupid, pushed the calfs on top of the dwarves and stole the loafs in the panic. The dwarfs flounced off saying,

"That's it. You'll have to sort it out yourselfs."

Nothing is too much trouble — except homework...

Little known fact about plurals — they *NEVER*, repeat *NEVER* need an apostrophe. Not even words ending in 'y'. *NOT EVEN* words ending in a vowel. 1 Mary → 2 Marys, 1 banana → 2 bananas. Yup.

Word Endings

*A word ending is called a suffix, like in improv**ing**, improv**able** and improve**ment**. Other suffixes are **-ful**, and **-ly**.*

Suffixes beginning with vowels
*Look at the last letter of the words in italics. If it's **a**, **i**, **o** or **u**, just add the suffix. If it's **e**, you have to get rid of it before adding the suffix.*

***E**s don't like sharing space with vowels on suffixes — show them an **-ing**, an **-ible**, an **-able** or even an **-ed** and they run away and hide.*

Q1 a) Copy out the words from the box that are spelt correctly:

Cure	curable	cureable
Video	videoing	videing
Excite	exciteed	excited
Notice	noticeing	noticing
Response	responseible	responsible
Shake	shaking	shakeing
Love	loveable	lovable
Taxi	taxid	taxied

Shania was unimpressable

b) Match up five of the word roots below with a suffix from the box. Use your words to make five sentences of your own.

describe move ski age sense manage adore debate echo

-ing -ible -able -ed

Q2 Copy out the sentences below, adding the right suffix to the word root (shown in italics).

*If your suffix begins with a consonant, the silent **e** is happy — it can stay. It likes **-ful**, **-ly** and **-ment**.*

a) She was *care* not to disturb anyone as she crept in.
b) At ten to four, everyone had gone home and the school was *peace*.
c) He *desperate* wanted to be allowed to go on the trip.
d) Finishing the race in such a short time was a tremendous *achieve*.
e) Don't throw that away, it could be *use*.
f) He was a good *advertise* for his school.
g) You must measure ingredients *accurate* or the recipe won't work.

Word Endings

*When adding a suffix to words ending in **y** — look at the letter in front of the **y**.*

*If it's a vowel, keep the **y**. If it's a consonant, change the **y** to an **i**.*
*If you're adding **-ing**, the **y** stays, no matter what comes in front of it.*

Exception alert. Learn these exceptions to the rules —
day becomes **daily**, lay becomes **laid**, pay becomes **paid**,
say becomes **said** *and* slay becomes **slain**.

Q1 Write these sentences out correctly (watch out for the exceptions):

a) I was enjoing the lesson so much I didn't hear the bell.
b) I'm hungryer than an empty alligator.
c) Her ambition was to start her own hamster-grooming busyness.
d) Their neighbour's late-night trumpet plaing was becoming a bit of a problem.
e) The hen liked to let everyone know when it had layed an egg.
f) He disliked being reminded of his win in the prettyest baby competition.
g) We need someone relyable to do our homework for us.
h) His habit of keeping ferrets in his pockets made him rather unemploiable.
i) The dog wasn't allowed on the chair until her coat had dryed.

***-cian**, **-sion** and **-tion** — they all sound like 'shun' but how do you know which to use?*
*If you have to guess, use **-tion** because that's the most common.*

*Occasion and collision are the two words ending in **-sion** that you're most likely to need.*

Q2 Write out these sentences with the correct word ending (if you're not sure, go for the one that looks right):

a) The mocian/mosion/motion of the roller coaster made him very sick.
b) We'll make this land into a great nasion/nation/nacian, cried the polititión/politisian/politician.
c) His collition/collision/collician with the wall didn't do his nose much good.
d) It was a special occasion/occation/occacian.
e) I must go to the optition/optician/optision to get my eyes checked.
f) Trying to escape attencian/attention/attension by crawling under the desk rarely works.
g) A quarter of New Zealand's population/populacian/populasion lives in Auckland.

*Words ending in **-cian** are often used for someone with a special skill, like magi**cian**, electri**cian** or musi**cian**.*

I'd rather hear about page endings...

Attention! You're about as likely to find a word ending in -tian as you are to meet a Martian walking a Dalmatian making friends with an Egyptian whose Christian name is Jake. No really.

Prefixes

A prefix is the opposite of a suffix — it's comes at the beginning of a word.

un- *and* ***in-*** *are useful for changing the meaning of a word to the opposite of what it meant before. e.g. happy becomes* ***un****happy.*

There's no rule, but ***un-*** is much more common.

Q1 Write out these words, using ***un-*** or ***in-*** to turn them into their opposite:

a) happy
b) clean
c) active
d) broken
e) visible
f) cover
g) dress
h) fair

These are some less common but useful prefixes which do the same job — ***il-****,* ***im-*** *and* ***ir-****.*

If the word begins with ***l****, use* ***-il****.*
If the word begins with ***b****,* ***m*** *or* ***p****, use* ***-im****.*
If the word begins with ***r****, usually you use* ***-ir****.*

Q2 a) Choose the right prefix for each of these words:

resistible legible possible patient mature legal

b) Write out these sentences, using each of the words in a) to fill the gaps:

i) "I can't do this. It's .... ," thought Julie.
ii) A six year old driving a bus would be ....
iii) I'm trying to diet, but that ice cream is just ....
iv) "You're so ....," she snapped at the boys who were trying to put a worm down her neck.
v) Don't be so .... ! She'll be here in a minute.
vi) I can't read this — your writing is completely ....

Top tip box — as seen previously on page six...

'Pre-' means 'before'. It comes from a Latin word "prae" that means 'beforehand' or 'in front'. It's used loads, like in *pre*-school or *pre*historic — or the Department of *Pre*crime in *Minority Report*.

Spelling Rules

Q1 Match each group of words below with the right spelling rule (A to H). (Some words appear in more than one list.)

a) business, chocolate, imaginary, guard, interesting, listening, marriage, necessary, reference, secondary, separate, Wednesday
b) concentration, decide, necessary, participation, peaceful, process, receive
c) actually, lonely, lovely, sincerely, surely, unfortunately, peaceful, assessment, development, engagement, environment
d) continue ➔ continuous, nerve ➔ nervous, imagine ➔ imaginary, second ➔ secondary
e) beauty ➔ beautiful, bury ➔ buried, busy ➔ business, industry ➔ industrial, marry ➔ marriage, priority ➔ prioritise
f) conclusion, decision, persuasion, possession
g) accommodation, concentration, creation, evaluation, explanation, participation, preparation, proportion, proposition, reaction

A) Suffixes which begin with a consonant don't usually change the end of a word — if there's an **e** on the end, it stays there.
B) An **i** or an **e** after a **c** make it soft.
C) When the end of a word sounds like 'shun', the soluTION is usually **-TION**.
D) Word endings — if there's a consonant in front of the **y**, change the **y** to an **i** when adding a suffix.
E) Some words have vowels that never do any work, which makes them unstressed vowels.
F) Suffixes which begin with vowels — they don't usually change the end of a word unless it's an **e**, then it has to go.
G) When the end of a word sounds like 'shun', occaSIONally it's spelled **-SION**.

Q2 Write out these sentences, choosing the right words from each pair of brackets:

a) I'm going to give you a piece of *(advise/advice)*.
b) The room was so *(quiet/quite)* you could hear the sound of people breathing.
c) Sal was never *(allowed/aloud)* to wear what she wanted to parties.
d) They put all their money together and *(bought/brought)* a life-size model of a donkey.
e) There *(our/are)* nearly 60 million people living in the United Kingdom.
f) Seven pizzas would be *(to/too/two)* many *(to/too/two)* eat in one go.
g) She was in trouble when she *(threw/through)* the cake *(through/threw)* the window.
h) Watching the end of the film made them late for football *(practise/practice)*.
i) My heart is *(braking/breaking)*, she thought, as she watched him walk away.
j) Lack of exercise has a bad *(effect/affect)* on your health.

Why did the dinosaurs die? — because I shot them...

Yup, this stuff's tedious alright. That's spelling for you. But learn these rules and it'll save you a bucketload of hassle (and red pen) from your stressed-out teacher. Come on, how hard can it be.

Apostrophes

Apostrophes have two jobs —

One — they show that a letter is missing when a word is shortened (e.g. ***what's*** *instead of* ***what is****). Two — they show that something belongs to something else (like the* ***dog's*** *dinner).*

Q1 Write out these sentences, putting the apostrophe in the right place — where there are letters missing. The first three show you which word needs the apostrophe:

a) I think *thats* the best thing that ever happened to me.
b) You *dont* all have to shout at once.
c) *Youre* the fastest worker I ever saw.
d) When they finish theyll come over here.
e) I cant believe you remembered my birthday.
f) Do you know whos won the cup?

Q2 Write out these sentences, showing how to shorten words using apostrophes. The first three show you which words to shorten:

Be careful with the last two — you have to <u>change</u> some of the letters, as well as getting rid of some.

a) You know you *cannot* ride down there without falling off.
b) If Jo asks Simon, *he will* come with us.
c) *That is* all, folks!
d) We are going out to the cinema later.
e) All of that lot think they are better than everyone else.
f) I will not come home late, I promise.
g) I shall not give it back until you say sorry.

Q3 Use apostrophes with an s to change the clumsy phrases below into a quicker way of saying the same thing.

e.g. — the head belonging to the man = the man's head.

If the owner ends in ***s*** *already, you can just add the apostrophe without the* ***s*** *i.e. the car belonging to Chris = Chris' car*

There was some confusion over which was the man's head.

a) the hutch belonging to the rabbit
b) the football belonging to Nat
c) the scar belonging to Carlos
d) the wheel belonging to the truck
e) the leg belonging to the horse
f) the label belonging to the video
g) the edge belonging to the cliff

Sometimes you need an apostrophe even when it's hard to see how something could belong to something else — Sunday's game, in a second's time.

The horse has one leg — why doesn't he fall over...

When you shorten a word and miss out letters, it's sometimes called an <u>omission</u> or a <u>contraction</u>. Hmm... Actually, you probably won't ever need to know those words, but just think how impressive it'd be if you managed to drop them casually into conversation. Just think how brainy you'd sound.

Apostrophes

*If a word ends in **s** because it's a plural —
you don't need another **s** when you add an apostrophe.*

e.g. plurals like boys, babies, churches etc...

Q1 Add apostrophes to these sentences where needed:

a) It's the boys turn to go first because the girls went first last time.
b) He was never allowed to forget the time he went into the ladies changing room by mistake.
c) Put all the babies pictures together so we can pick out a winner.
d) People always seem to find footballers haircuts very interesting.
e) The nurses meeting went on for three hours.
f) We'll be there in two hours time.

*It's easier when a plural doesn't end in **s** — then you go back to normal and add an apostrophe and an **s**.*

e.g. the electricity coming from lots of bison → the bison's electricity
the nest of a family of mice → the mice's nest

Q2 Match the word to the sentence, using apostrophes to show ownership:

children sheep men lice aircraft

a) I don't know why ..... toilets are always smellier than women's.
b) Our house is right under a flight path so we can hear the ..... engines all night.
c) The sponsored walk raised £300 for the ..... playground.
d) In my story, a boy had to eat seven ..... eyes
e) Head..... size and colour make them difficult to see in anyone's hair.

*There are some words that **don't** need an apostrophe when they're showing ownership. They are possessive pronouns — **mine, yours, his, hers, ours, theirs, its**.*

Q3 Write these sentences out correctly:

watch out — they're not all wrong

a) I've got my lunch, but I didn't pick your's up.
b) Jon said the book was his' but Sunita said it was her's.
c) I'm sure its hurt, its got its wing stretched out.
d) Tom's drawing is bigger, but I think mine's better.
e) When we've finished rehearsing, they'll perform their's first and then we'll do ours'.

Own up — who left the bison running last night...

It's something everyone gets wrong. Don't tell me you don't know what it is.
IT IS or IT HAS becomes IT'S SOMETHING BELONGING TO IT becomes ITS.
Copy this out ten times: "Look at that bison — it's got its hat on." Now do it without the book.

Familiar Words

Below are three words from each subject that people often spell badly.

Q1 a) Choose your three favourite subjects and copy out the correct spelling for each word. (But do the English one as an extra one — this is an English book after all...)

b) Use a dictionary to check the meaning of each word. Write it out in your own words.

Art
perspectife or perspective
colour or color
dimension or dimention

Drama
character or carachter
curtein or curtain
theater or theatre

Geography
amenitey or amenity
country or countrey
wether or weather

ICT
justify or justifie
cursor or curser
sensers or sensors

Maths
symmetrey or symmetry
equasion or equation
isosceles or isoscelese

PE
athlete or athelete
mussle or muscle
exercise or exorcise

RS
religeous or religious
immorality or imorrality
spirituel or spiritual

D and T
hygeine or hygiene
ingredient or ingrediant
desine or design

English
advertisement or advertisment
sentance or sentence
consonant or consonent

History
invation or invasion
defence or defense
seige or siege

Library
article or artical
glossery or glossary
editor or editer

Music
percussion or precussion
instrumant or instrument
rhythm or rhythem

PSHE
generousity or generosity
pressurise or pressureise
involvment or involvement

Science
labratory or laboratory
apparatus or aparatus
solutian or solution

I said no — you can't spell school with a "z"...

Remember to use the spelling rules to help you — but watch out for the exceptions. Nothing's easy in this life. If it was, I'd be in the Bahamas with a massive pile of cash right now...

Sounding Out

Q1 The words in the box below have been broken down into sounds which form them. Match the correct set of sounds to the correct word.

alcohol, although, people, caught, fierce, fulfil, happened, surprise, shoulder, strength, texture, knowledge

a) ce-ie-r-f
b) h-l-o-a-l-o-c
c) x-u-t-t-re-e
d) e-dge-kn-l-ow
e) r-th-ng-t-s-e
f) augh-t-c
g) d-sh-l-ou-er
h) i-f-f-l-u-l
i) ed-h-pp-a-e-n
j) th-ough-l-a
k) eo-le-p-p
l) r-se-ur-s-i-p

Q2 Write out these sentences and fill in the missing syllables:

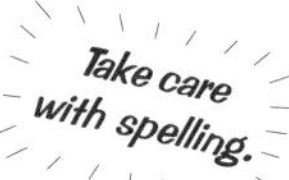

a) She wrote in her jour... every day for thir.. years.
b) Lee ..cided it would cause too much embarr...ment to announce his feelings in front of everyone.
c) The younger you are, the more ..terest you have in looking after the en..ronment.
d) The sides of a square or ...tangle are pa..llel.
e) Everyone on the trip must re...ber a packed lunch.
f) No ... ever list... to what their moth.. tells them.

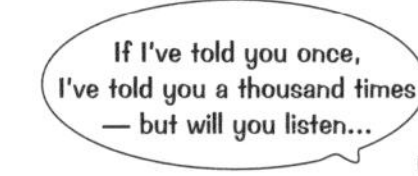

Q3 Sort the words in the box into three groups under the following headings — One Syllable, Two Syllables and Three Syllables.

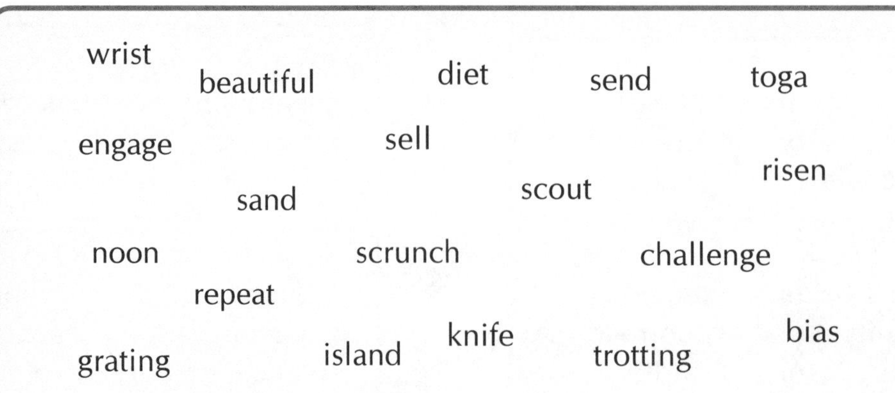

Sounding so like that — like, huh, whatEVER, yeah...

This is all about how words sound — so it'll help if you say them out loud. Well, obviously not while you're at the cinema, or waiting at the doctor's or anything. That'd be dead embarrassing.

Using Words You Know

Q1 a) Write out the sentences below, filling the gaps with letter strings from the box — you **only need one** for each sentence. (If there are any words you don't know, look them up in a dictionary.)

ound ough air aught tual ight

i) The br.... l.... in the middle of the n.... gave the kn.... a r.... fr..... .
ii) Dancing was a habi.... part of the ac.... ri.... .
iii) His d.....er was t..... that l.....er was the wrong response to sl.....er.
iv) He c....ed as he pl....ed thr.... the t.... tr....s and r.... b....s.
v) The ast....ing s.... of the b....ing h.... surr....ed the m.... that they stood ar..... .
vi) The rep... of the ch... brought desp... to the h...y f...y.

b) Now make up your own sentence for each of the groups of words below. Try to use as many as you can in each sentence.

i) own, grown, sown, mown, known
ii) shoulder, boulder, smoulder, moulder
iii) hunch, crunch, bunch, lunch, munch, punch

Q2 Make as many words as you can from each of the root words below by adding suffixes and prefixes. (There's some prefixes and suffixes in the box below to get you started.)

a) vent b) phone c) bit d) trap e) trail f) sign g) rage h) fan

e.g. root word = press.
pressure, impress, impression, impressive, depress, depressing, depressingly

-able -age -al -ant -ary -cy -ed -ely -eme -en -ent -er
es -ful/-full -ible -ier -ily -ing -is -ise -ist -ly -ment -ory
-ry -tion -ure -al/-all de- en- em- for- in- im- il- ir-

Q3 Use the information in the table to work out/guess the meaning of the following difficult words. Write down your definitions.

a) mortician (American word) b) philanthropist c) orthodox

Word	Meaning	Origin
Doxa	opinion	Greek
Anthropos	human being	Greek
Mortis	death	Latin
Philos	loving	Greek
Ortho	straight	Greek

Check Your Spelling

Q1 a) Identify the word that is misspelt in the each of these groups and write it out correctly:

i) receive / believe / thief / decieve
ii) boys / puppies / donkies / robberies
iii) addresses / schools / tables / torchs
iv) sheeps / deer / aircraft / fish
v) robbing / running / swiming / sobbing

b) For each bit of part a), write down the relevant spelling rule that has been broken.

Q2 Write out each sentence choosing the correct word:

a) Thank you. I would be delighted to *accept / except* your invitation.
b) Although he tried *quiet / quite* hard, Jack did not make the football team.
c) Can you please *write / right* a letter to the prime minister?
d) Bryony *new / knew* the answer before the teacher had finished asking the question.
e) Are they taking *their / there* dog on holiday with them?

Q3 Now write five sentences of your own, using the words that you didn't choose for Q2.

Q4 Some of the sentences below are correct, but others contain a misspelt word. Say whether each sentence is right or wrong, and rewrite the incorrect ones.

a) I've been practicing my juggling skills for months.
b) Can't you give me any advice?
c) Jimbo ran passed the lion-tamer with a smile.
d) Where are gran's leg warmers now?
e) I always come last at spelling-practice.
f) There's a bomblike devise strapped to the hymn book.
g) I past my exams really easily.
h) Their just aren't enough good hairdressers in the world.
i) I have devised a new type of electric guinea pig.
j) Were are the best places to eat toffee around here?

Spellbinding? — no, spelling rules aren't THAT good...

Mmm — yet more tricky words. The way to learn spellings is: 1) Copy it out a few times. 2) Get used to what it looks like spelt right. 3) Get a blank page and write it again from memory.

Tricky Spellings

Here is a list of 20 tricky spellings.

1. dependent
2. psychology
3. successful
4. responsible
5. people
6. receive
7. separate
8. necessary
9. monarchy
10. misspelt
11. beautiful
12. permanent
13. immediately
14. accommodation
15. keep
16. psychiatrist
17. fortunately
18. convenient
19. definite
20. irregular

Q1 All of the words in the list are described by one of the sentences below. Say which words fall under which heading. I've done the first one for you.

a) 'ch' is pronounced as 'k'

a) psychology, monarchy, psychiatrist

watch out — some appear in more than one category

b) adverbs that were adjectives before 'ly' was added
c) adjectives which end in 'ent'
d) the first syllable is pronounced 'sigh'
e) words having surprising double consonants
f) use of 'i' where 'a' would seem more obvious
g) adjectives that were nouns before 'ful' was added
h) a word that follows a spelling rule involving 'i' and 'e'
i) use of 'a' where 'e' would seem more obvious
j) a word in which 'u' is pronounced 'w'
k) a word which has an 'o' which is unpronounced

Q2 Write down one word of your own for categories a) to g) in Q1.

It was a tricky spell and Melvin wasn't sure he'd made things better.

It's necessary to separate the monarch from the psychiatrist...

Eeeuch — some real nasty beggars in here. 'Fraid there's nothing for it. It's either learn these spellings or watch TV. No, wait... It's either learn these spellings or eat raw cabbage. Just do it, OK.

Varied Vocabulary

Q1 a) Write out sentences i) - v), choosing the most appropriate 'eating' word from the box below.

nibbled   devoured   gnawed   munched   masticated

i) Daniel .... his meal hungrily but with great enjoyment.
ii) Maria .... her chocolate bar slowly as she watched the film.
iii) The dog .... every scrap of meat off the bone.
iv) She .... her chewing gum in a disgusting manner.
v) That horse .... its way through three bundles of hay today.

b) Look up each of the above words in a dictionary and use it in a sentence of your own.

Q2 Write each group of adjectives in order of strength of feeling from strongest to weakest.

a) huge / enormous / large / mammoth
b) miniscule / little / microscopic / tiny
c) ecstatic / pleased / satisfied / delighted

Q3 Write a sentence of your own using each of the adjectives below. Use a dictionary to help you with the difference in meanings.

a) heartbroken
b) downhearted
c) distressed
d) depressed

Q4 Two of the most overused words are 'nice' and 'good'. Rewrite this passage replacing these words with words that are more descriptive:

Yesterday was a really good day. I went with a group of nice friends to see a really good film. It was a good film because it had lots of action and really good actors. After the film we went to a nice café and had a good time. The food was really nice and we all had really good-sized portions. It was especially good when the nice monkey ate my napkin. It was one of my nicest days ever.

Always use varied vocabulary / language / words...

Pretty darned useful, those thesaurususes. (Thesauri, I think it ought to be.) Anyway... Learn how to use a thesaurus properly — using varied vocabulary will improve your essays no end.

Investigating Words

Q1 Use a thesaurus to look up these words.
Write down all the entries listed under each one.

a) skip
b) row
c) jump
d) fray
e) mass

Q2 a) Choose five of the words you found in Q1 a). For each one, use a dictionary to give the following information about each entry:

i) pronunciation
ii) part of speech
iii) one meaning of the word
iv) the origin of the word

b) Do the same for 5 of the entries you found for Q1 b).

Q3 Many words in English come from other languages. Write next to each of the following English words which language it comes from. Choose from the list in the box.

a) joey
....

b) restaurant
....

c) balcony
....

d) caravan
....

e) bungalow
....

f) coffee
....

g) yacht
....

h) chocolate
....

i) microbe
....

j) tepee
....

Nahuatl	*chocolatl*
Sioux	*tipi*
Persian	*karwan*
Aboriginal	*joe*
Italian	*balcone*
Arabic	*kahwa*
Hindustani	*bungla*
Greek	*mikros* (small) *bios* (life)
French	*restaurer* (to restore)
Dutch	*jaghte*

School: academy, college, institution, form of torture...

A thesaurus gives you loads of alternative words, but some of them only work in certain situations. If you're in any doubt about how to use a word you find in a thesaurus, look it up in a dictionary.

Word Workout

Many English words have Greek and Latin roots.

Bits of English words from Greek and Latin:

audio	*(to hear)*	*geo*	*(earth)*	*metre*	*(measure)*
bio	*(life)*	*gram*	*(small weight)*	*phone*	*(voice/sound)*
chromo	*(colour)*	*graph*	*(writing)*	*photo*	*(light)*
chrono	*(time)*	*logo*	*(word/reason)*	*scope*	*(target)*
				sphere	*(ball)*

Q1 Below are some prefixes from Greek and Latin. Look up the prefixes in a dictionary to find out exactly what they mean. (Look at the origin of the word to find out.)

A __prefix__ is a group of letters fixed to the front of a word. ('Pre' comes from Latin and means 'before'.)

a) ante –
b) anti –
c) bi –
d) com –
e) en –/in –
f) epi –
g) ex –
h) hyper–
i) hypo –
j) inter –
k) mal –
l) mega –
m) micro –
n) mono –
o) penta –
p) poly –
q) post –
r) pro –
s) re –
t) sub –
u) super –
v) syn –
w) tele –
x) tetra –
y) tri –
z) uni –

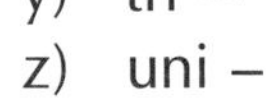

Q2 Take the roots and prefixes from Greek and Latin in Q1, and make a common English word from each of them, e.g. microscope, bicycle, subzero.

Watch out — trickier question follows shortly...

Q3 Guess what the following words mean. For each word, write down your guess, then check it in a dictionary. If you were wrong, write down the correct meaning.

a) anteroom
b) biofuel
c) tetrapod
d) hypoacidity
e) photodegradable
f) monochromatic
g) maladjusted
h) polychromatic
i) antilogy
j) polyphone
k) telescience
l) synchronise

Hint — use the stuff on the rest of the page to help you.

I dunno — it's all Greek to me...

It's not surprising that English spelling is so random. It's made up of so many bits of other languages that there's no way we were ever going to end up with something nice and consistent. Still, spelling-test nightmares aside, you can't deny it makes for a pretty interesting language.

Know Your Language

Q1 Match each type of word to its correct definition in this table:

Type of Word:	Definition:
noun	joins two sentences or parts of a sentence
verb	describes a noun
auxiliary verb	introduces a noun
adjective	helps the main verb in the sentence
adverb	introduces a phrase about time or place
preposition	describes a verb
conjunction	is a person, place or thing
article	is a doing or being word

Q2 For each of the following underlined words, write down what type of word it is (e.g. noun, preposition, etc.).

a) Francesca wore a hideous dress to the party.
b) Carlos rides a bicycle to school every day.
c) The key is in the cupboard under the stairs.
d) The cat and dog were friends but they liked to tease each other.
e) The old man chose an apple and a peach from the bowl.
f) The player kicked the ball hard but accurately.
g) Tamsin skated across the ice then gracefully crashed into the wall.
h) After Paul had finished his tea and was deciding what to do next, his head exploded.
i) The boxer was exhausted but elated after winning the fight.

Q3 Copy out this list of words. Next to each word, write a sentence using at least one of that type of word — and underline each one.

noun: *"It's odd," remarked Chrissy, "I don't recognise that snail."* ← *'snail' is a noun — and so is 'Chrissy'*
main verb:
auxiliary verb:
adjective:
adverb:
preposition:
conjunction:
article:

"Grandma, what [adjective] [noun] [pronoun] [verb]"*

It's not exactly rip-roaring fun, but you've got to learn all these technical terms. These questions are great practice, so no shirking. Once you can do all these, pat yourself on the back and move on.

* "Grandma, what big teeth you have." Taken from a popular children's fairytale. You may recognise it.

Qualifications and Comparisons

Q1 Copy out the following sentences, underlining the qualifying words being used in each one.

Qualifications can be used to clarify things or give more detail.

e.g. It is hard to understand completely why he shaved off his eyebrows.

a) They mostly attack after dark.
b) You might guess from her squint that she is partially sighted.
c) Teenagers hardly ever pay attention to their elders.
d) I think you will find that you are slightly mistaken.
e) He can usually be found hiding under the bed, with his eyes closed.

Q2 For each of these words, write a sentence of your choice using the word as a qualifier:

a) normally
b) rarely
c) similarly
d) sometimes
e) habitually
f) typically
g) relatively
h) possibly
i) periodically

Q3 Write out these comparative sentences, completing them using examples of your choice.

e.g. The Sahara Desert has the smallest number of icebergs in the world.

a) There are fewer .... in my school than ....

b) The .... has the most .... I've ever seen in my life!

c) There are fewer .... in the sea than ....

d) The more .... you invite to your party, the merrier the .... will be.

e) That .... saw the least amount of .... in a long time.

Q4 Write a sentence using each pair of comparative terms below. You must not refer to the same subject more than once.

a) faster / slowest
e.g. I run faster than Leo, even though I'm the slowest runner in my class.
b) heavier / lightest
c) quieter / loudest
d) prettier / ugliest
e) weaker / strongest

Terms of comparison draw attention to similarities and differences between things.

This is the most interestingestish page in the book...

Well, quite. It's a laugh isn't it, this English malarkey. Hmm... hot tips... let me think... ah, yes — here's one *everyone* gets wrong: if you use "more" or "most" before a comparing word, you *DON'T* need "-er" or "-est" on the end of it. E.g. it'd be "more cool" or "cooler", but NOT "more cooler".

Playing with Words

You can add '-ify' to an adjective to create a verb.
e.g. Is this a just cause? Can you honestly justify this cause?
Sometimes you need to knock a bit off the original word first.
e.g. What is this signal? What does it signify?

Q1 Change each of the highlighted nouns and adjectives into a verb:

a) I have an awful feeling that this information is all **false**.
b) The **testimony** of this witness is definitely suspect.
c) The Queen's Golden Jubilee is for the **glorification** of her reign.
d) Just how **specific** does our analysis have to be?
e) What **magnification** do we need to achieve the best results?

Verb → Noun:

You can change verbs into nouns by adding '-ence' or '-tion' (knocking a bit off the end first).
e.g. contribute — contribution.

Remember — letters added to the end of a word to make a new one are called 'suffixes'.

Q2 Change each of these verbs into nouns by adding **either** '-ence' **or** '-tion':

a)	interfere	c)	dedicate	e)	persist	g)	participate	i)	elevate
b)	exist	d)	graduate	f)	insist	h)	complicate	j)	refer

Noun → Verb:

Adding '-ise' (or '-ize') to a noun also creates a new verb.
(Once again, sometimes knocking the end off first.)
e.g. noun = idol verb = idolize (or idolise)

Q3 Write down the verbs that are related to nouns in these sentences.
For each one, also write down the corresponding noun.

All of these verbs could be spelt '-ise' and they'd still be right. It's a funny old language...

a) In my darkest dreams, I fantasize about a world without limits.
b) "You can hypothesize all you want but I am not putting my underpants on my head."
c) It's all very well to criticize but it's not your job at stake.
d) If you don't publicize what you're capable of, how will anyone know what you can do?

Q4 Make other words from the following by placing **re-**, **un-**, **dis-** or **de-** in front of them:

e.g. natural — unnatural.

a)	tidy	d)	apply	g)	balanced		
b)	part	e)	wind	h)	sanitary	j)	code
c)	satisfaction	f)	approve	i)	connect	k)	hinged

Remember — letters added to the start of a word to make a different one are called 'prefixes'.

Not sure about this stuff — it's a bit -ify...

Never underestimate the power of a wide vocabulary. The stuff on this page is *really handy* for turning a good word into a good, *usable* word for you to stick in your essays. Teachers are dead impressed if you use loads of interesting words and it will improve your marks.

Using Linking Words

Saying when something happens helps people work out the order of events. It's done using linking words or phrases, such as 'later' or 'at the same time as'.

e.g. Later that day, we began to notice a change in the buffalo.

Q1 Write out the following sentences, underlining the linking words.

a) During the second half of the play, my nose started to run and my ear began to itch.
b) Whilst she remained perfectly still, I ran up and down screaming "Emergency!"
c) Meanwhile, down in the cellar, all was not well.
d) Just before midnight we heard a bloodcurdling scream from the laundry.
e) I can honestly say that I was fast asleep for the whole time.

You can also link phrases to show why something happened, using linking words like 'because' and 'despite the fact that'.

e.g. Although I couldn't see what the problem was, I agreed to untie her hands.

Q2 Write a sentence using each of these linking words and phrases:

a) so
b) because
c) since
d) understandably
e) as a direct result
f) clearly
g) obviously
h) as expected
i) unquestionably

And finally... Linking words can be used to say what could happen, or give opinions.

e.g. Call me a cynic, but I reckon the Millennium Dome won't last for a whole millennium.

Q3 Complete the following sentences in any way you choose.

a) Perhaps I'm being superstitious but...
b) My granny always said you could never tell about salesmen because...
c) I began to speculate on how she'd managed...
d) It was possible now to guess what...
e) We can only imagine what went through his head when...

Q4 Write a paragraph on any subject, using links of time, cause and speculation to make your text more effective as a whole.

eeeesh — rather you than me...

Linking words — ALWAYS handy...

Yeah. I know. It's kinda weird breaking everything down and explaining it. But get a good grip on all these little bits, and your work will be tons better than it was before. I promise.

Putting Words into Context

Q1 You would expect to use the following terms in a science lesson. Write a sentence with each of them, placing the words into an everyday context.

e.g. energy 'I was getting tired — three miles non-stop and I'd run out of energy.'

a) resistance
b) reaction
c) experiment
d) equipment

Words on their own can often have a variety of meanings. Once you put a word into a sentence (into 'context'), there's usually just one meaning.

Q2 All the underlined words in the examples below can be used in both everyday speech and in academic subjects. For each one, say what subject it could come from and give an example of how it might be used.

a) The evidence would suggest he was hit over the head, with a turnip, in the library.
e.g. 'evidence' could be used in a history lesson to prove a point.
b) Formula One racing resembles sitting on a rocket and lighting the fuse.
c) "Young man, your vocabulary leaves a lot to be desired!" growled the crusty old hag.
d) You can see the whole city from the observation tower.
e) "I've spent fourteen years in a tiny prison cell, just waiting to see you."

Q3 Write a sentence in an everyday context, using words you would associate with each of these specific subjects. **Don't** use any words from the previous questions.

a) History
b) Geography
c) Science
d) English

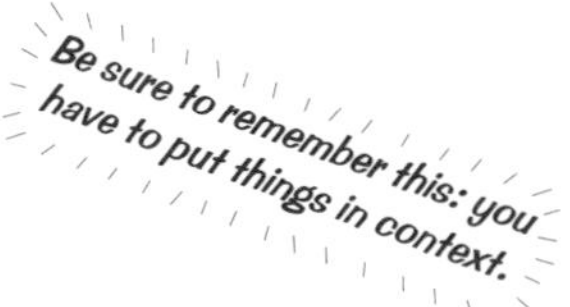

Context — isn't that a South London train company...

Context is all-important. Imagine seeing a polar bear in Swindon. (You see where I'm going here.) Anyway, it's the same with words. E.g. 'balance' might mean one thing to a physicist, but it means something very different to an accountant — and yet another thing entirely to a tightrope walker...

Using Clauses

Q1 Write out the completed sentences by joining the clauses to make a whole sentence:

a) My brother is happy
b) As the plane takes off
c) He stopped reading
d) Whenever he chased his tail,
e) Although she felt sad,

...she sang at the concert
...the dog ran in circles
...I watch the wings vibrate
...because the monster was making him scared
...when his team wins

Q2 Write out the following sentences and underline the subordinate clause:

The subordinate clause depends on the main clause of a sentence:

Tim chatted to the housemates, straightening his hair.

Without the main clause its meaning is incomplete, so it is called 'subordinate'.

a) Keen to go home, Roy threw a tantrum.
b) Speaking from his heart, he displayed how he really felt.
c) My barber, who was very wealthy, cut his prices.
d) Whenever it snows, the mountains look beautiful.
e) The DVD, which I bought yesterday, was already damaged.
f) Until the bridge was built, people crossed the river by boat.

Q3 Use each of these words to write a sentence:

a) after
b) whenever
c) since
d) before
e) until
f) like
g) for
h) if
i) because
j) however
k) despite

Q4 Complete each of these sentences by adding a **wh** (who, which, where) clause where shown:

a) I've just bought Rap 212's new album [wh...] is awful.
b) It's for my best friend John [wh...] lives in New York.
c) It was in Devon [wh...] there was a terrible outbreak of Foot and Mouth disease.
d) I meant that bottle of lemonade [wh...] has probably gone flat.
e) Sarah, [wh...] is packing for her holidays, is a bit tired.

This is terrifying — I feel quite clause-trophobic...

Variety is the spice of life — so they say... And varied sentence length is the spice of essays. Use some long sentences, adorned with many colourful subordinate clauses. Keep some short and sweet. Mix it up a bit — and your essays will be wonderful. Which, I can tell, you're thrilled to bits about.

Using Clauses

Q1 Combine each pair of sentences into one sentence containing a subordinate clause:

a) John was travelling by train. He was going to visit his grandma.
b) Sabrina chose to walk to the party. She was wearing her favourite dress.
c) The dog growled at the man. It moved closer to him.
d) She opened the door of the cage. She hoped her pet was still inside.
e) The manager was in a desperate hole. He mumbled that it was a game of two halves.

Q2 Write a sentence with a subordinate clause, using each of the following words to start it:

a) Going...
b) Having...
c) Staying...
d) Wearing...
e) Wanting...

Q3 Choose five **-ing** words of your own to begin or end a sentence with a subordinate clause.

Q4 Write these sentences out again, putting the clauses in a different place in the sentence:

a) He wears his swimming goggles while chopping onions.
e.g. While chopping onions, he wears his swimming goggles.
b) Like all fiends, she had a devilish grin.
c) Despite losing all his matches, he burned to play again.
d) Do not add the celery until the onions turn a golden brown.
e) When the bell rings, everyone must evacuate the building.

Q5 Look at the following sentences. Into each insert a subordinate clause that uses **who**, **when**, **where** or **which**.

a) The knife was sharp.
b) Henry wanted an eighth course.
c) In America they play baseball.
d) The detective drove to the scene of the crime.
e) Diana laughed at the joke.
f) On Friday we will feed the penguins.
g) Dangerous creatures roamed the jungle.

Get your 'clause' in.

Making Nouns More Interesting

A noun phrase can be altered by adding adjectives to the noun:

The cat slept.
The fat, brown cat slept.

Q1 Rewrite each of these simple sentences, adding adjectives to make it more interesting:

a) The girl shouted.
b) A car crashed.
c) The boy cried.
d) The baby slept.
e) The alligator snapped.

Q2 Add a prepositional phrase to each of the sentences above.

e.g. The fat, brown cat slept.
The fat, brown cat slept on the bed.

Q3 Write out the following sentences and underline the prepositional phrases.

a) Bad Alice screamed at her brother.
b) The boy slumped over his literacy booklet.
c) The American soldiers landed at four o'clock.
d) He hurled the stone through the window.
e) His computer exploded with a bang.

Q4 Write out the complete sentences by joining the prepositional phrase to the main clause:

a)	The rabid dog leapt...	...into the rock
b)	Stanley arrived...	...to the garage before lunch
c)	She hid...	...at the crowd outside the kennels
d)	The sports car was delivered...	...behind the shed
e)	Tired and upset, the policeman bellowed...	...with his mum
f)	Leonardo, impatient to draw, scratched...	...at the burglar in the garden

It's a noun — a big, fat, hairy noun... on a stick...

A frog is pretty interesting, but not as interesting as a grotesque, warty frog. Don't be put off just because they've got a silly name — adjectives are cool. Yes they are. You should always look back at every sentence to see if there are any extra little details that would make it more interesting.

Punctuation

Q1 Writing that isn't punctuated properly can be difficult to understand. Write out these groups of sentences, adding punctuation or changing the punctuation so that it is correct.

a) Don't forget that tomorrow is sports day the whole school will be ending lessons after period three.
b) Tomorrow we're starting our project on newspapers don't forget to bring in a newspaper if you have one.
c) We've run out of tea can you get some from the shop on your way home.
d) The music was great though I'm not sure about the dancing, I don't think I could do all those high kicks.
e) Sheep are strange animals they're quite sweet though the lambs are particularly cute especially when they're very young.
f) When I was little we lived in the North people called you "luv" when they spoke to you then we moved further south.
g) He's fond of that desk because it was his grandfather's I bet it can tell some stories. His grandfather used to do all his letter-writing at that desk he was always writing to politicians and to the newspapers.

Q2 Some of these sentences have commas where no comma is needed. Some of the sentences need commas to make them clearer. Rewrite the sentences, with the correct punctuation.

a) Let me know, if you want to come.
b) Would the person who left their keys in the foyer, please collect them from reception?
c) I'll put you in touch with my elder sister who has a lot of experience in this area.
d) There are several new tracks many of which are completely different from the old stuff.
e) I met a lot of interesting people some of whom I really liked.
f) She told him, that she loved him.
g) My computer's not working which is a real pain.
h) She mentioned several things, that were bothering her.

Q3 Rewrite these paragraphs, using the punctuation marks in the box to make them easier to read. (Hint — you may need to replace punctuation, or add punctuation. Remember to use a capital letter if you start a new sentence.)

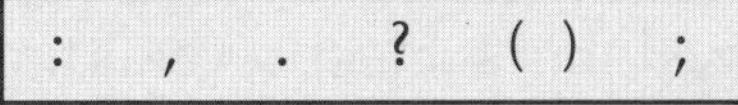

a) Next week we will be making meringues, you will need the following ingredients sugar and egg whites.
b) Oven temperature is very important in making meringues, it needs to be very low. If you are using an electric oven, you can turn it off after a certain amount of time and leave the meringues in the oven while it cools down
c) When your meringues are completely cool, you can sandwich them together with fresh cream alternatively you can drizzle melted chocolate over them
d) Can you think of alternative fillings for your meringues write your suggestions down in your notebook. You can write down something you have eaten before or something that you would like to try.

Using Verbs

Q1 It's important to use the correct tense of verbs if you want your writing to be clear. Write out these sentences, making changes to the tense of the verb where necessary.

a) He had been voted out by viewers who are fed up with his behaviour.
b) We had rung them to ask if they are coming the next day.
c) She can't promise to solve all of their problems, but she would try.
d) My printer had broken and so I need to go shopping.
e) What if no one would come?
f) The government is keen to explore various options and had decided to act as soon as possible.

Q2 The sentences in these paragraphs are in the wrong order. Write out the sentences in a sensible order. Put a number above each sentence, to show the order in which the events occurred.

More confusing than Prime Minister's Question Time eh? That's why I've done the first one for you...

a) He had sorted out the things I wanted. When I got there, I found him in his shed. Yesterday I went to see my uncle. I'd phoned him the day before to say I'd be coming.

e.g. *(3) Yesterday I went to see my uncle. (1) I'd phoned him the day before to say I'd be coming. (4) When I got there, I found him in his shed. (2) He had sorted out the things I wanted.*

b) They also said it would cost £200. They said they could only do it next week. So I'm going to ring round some other garages. I phoned the garage earlier about the car.
c) The party was a big success. Luckily we put it out quickly and the rest went smoothly. What no one realises is that the building almost caught fire an hour before everyone arrived. So much so, in fact, that it's been suggested it should be an annual event.
d) I'd watched the first half of it last week. Last night mum said I should have an evening without watching TV. I didn't agree, as I really wanted to see the concluding part of a particular programme.

Q3 Sometimes, what happens is more important than who does it. Rewrite these sentences, using a passive form to express what happened.

a) We have already discussed this subject several times.
e.g. *This subject has already been discussed several times*
b) We have introduced a new system.
c) We have forgotten several important points.
d) Several famous people have visited the school over the years.
e) They had cleaned the whole house from top to toe.
f) We all admired her.
g) I had washed their hair and scrubbed their faces.
h) We had interviewed all of the applicants.

Avoiding Ambiguity

Q1 The meaning of these sentences isn't 100% clear. For each sentence explain why it is confusing and write out a clearer version. Just on the off-chance that you're confused about what I mean, I've done the first one for you.

a) She had a sister and a dog; she was called Anna.

This is confusing because you don't know who is called Anna. It could mean the sister, or the dog, or the 'she' at the beginning of the sentence.
It would be clearer if it said: She had a sister and a dog; the dog was called Anna.

b) Could all those with young children return their forms as soon as possible.

c) The students asked the staff if they could help.

d) If you find any pictures of toys which are free, please bring them along.

Q2 Punctuation can change the meaning of words in a sentence. Look at these sentences, and write answers to the questions which follow.

a) However you do it, it's going to be tricky.
However, do it again and you're in trouble.

i) What does "however" mean in the first sentence?
ii) What does "however" mean in the second sentence?

b) She wants a designer name bag.
She wants a designer-name bag.

Why is the hyphen helpful in the second sentence?

c) In spite of this, interruption after interruption continued.
In spite of this interruption, the meeting continued.

In the first sentence, why is the comma after "this" helpful?

d) The book, which is published next week, should make her a lot of money.
The book which I gave you last week is actually Jill's.

Why are there commas in the first sentence, but not in the second sentence?

Q3 In the following paragraph there are four places where the meaning isn't immediately clear.

Sports Day is fun, although it can be rather embarrassing. When you're little your mum comes and cheers you on, makes you wear your sunhat (even though it's normally raining), and joins in the parents' races. Sometimes there's a teachers' race, too. By the time you get to senior school they usually stay at home, although you still have to participate whether you're sporty or not. The sixth formers are supposed to look after the younger ones, although they're usually not happy about this. At the end of the day, I think Sports Day should be optional and the rest of us should have the time off. After all the effort of organising it isn't necessarily matched by the amount of enjoyment it generates.

a) Write out the paragraph, changing the bits which aren't immediately clear.

b) Write down your reasons for the changes which you made.

Speech Punctuation

Q1 Rewrite the following sentences, adding speech marks where they're needed:

a) Have you got the sheepdog back yet? asked Jeremy.
b) Cathy looked a bit taken aback, but replied, No. The church was fine last time I looked.
c) Jess is lying down now. Mary sounded relieved and sat down.
d) I didn't know what to say; Oh, I muttered.
e) When is a raven like a writing desk? he asked us slowly, and how do you know?
f) Naz, if you don't give Adam's shoes back right now, he yelled, I swear you'll regret it.
g) Where, he asked, in a moment of silence, would you start looking for my handbag?

Q2 My friend Shania talks a lot. The phrases below are all things that she's said at some point, along with a word that describes how she felt at the time. Combine the two, writing the things she's said inside speech marks, as well as saying *how* she said them. I've done the first one for you.

a) Elton John's a ruddy marvellous singer. → passionate

a) "Elton John's a ruddy marvellous singer," said Shania passionately.

b) I think white stilettos are dead classy. → proud
c) Elvis is not dead. He's just resting. → serious
d) My uncle used to be a rabbit. → apologetic
e) Don't ever borrow my fishnets again. → angry and loud

Q3 Each of the sentences below have mistakes in their punctuation. Rewrite them so that they're correct.

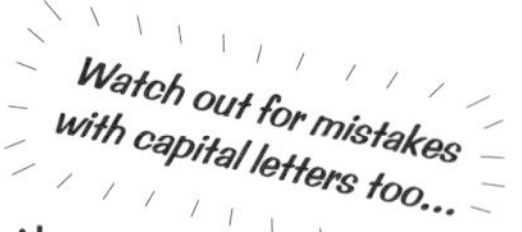

a) "I have been meaning to talk to you about that" he said with a smile.
b) Nasser wasn't sure how to respond. "maybe later" was just about all he could say.
c) "Haven't the penguins been sleeping in the tool shed," asked Marion in horror.
d) "I have a dream," she said, "and it involves a big plate of waffles.
e) "It wasn't me." she said, carefully slipping the goldfish back into the bowl.
f) "How exactly," he said looking mean, "do you think we're going to get to Fiji."
g) "It's not a question of who feeds him." Henry started. "It's a question of how much he gets fed." So that was that. "Unless we just go with the peanuts again." he added.

Talk is cheap — unless you have a parrot...

The most important thing about speech marks is to end each chunk with a full stop, comma, question mark or exclamation mark. Or cuttlefish. The punctuation goes *INSIDE* the speech marks.

Starting a New Paragraph

A new paragraph usually begins with an opening sentence to tell you what it's about.

Q1 **Match each opening sentence to its correct paragraph.**
You only need to write the letters (e.g. e) matches E — yep, it's that easy).

a) The fire engine raced down the busy street.
b) I looked up into the highest branches of the tree.
c) It was a cold January morning.
d) School uniform is another thing which children and their parents disagree about.

A

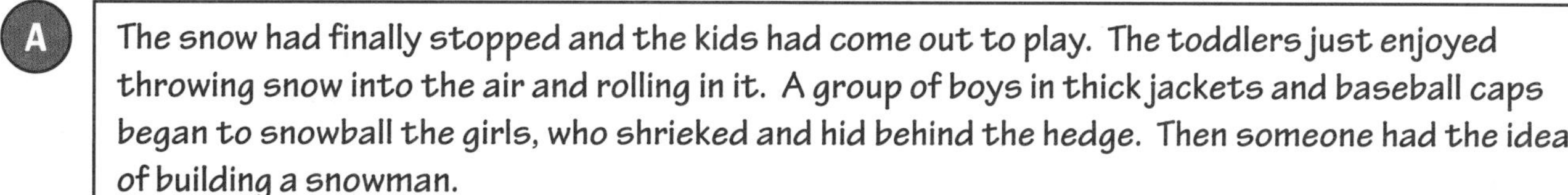
The snow had finally stopped and the kids had come out to play. The toddlers just enjoyed throwing snow into the air and rolling in it. A group of boys in thick jackets and baseball caps began to snowball the girls, who shrieked and hid behind the hedge. Then someone had the idea of building a snowman.

B

Smoke poured out of the upstairs windows and flames licked round the front door. A coughing policeman jumped out into the road and waved at the red fire engine. It screeched to a halt and the crew jumped into action.

C

The cat crept further out along the swaying branch. Austin was only a metre below, holding on with one hand while reaching up with the other. Other people stopped to watch, pointing up at the cat. Austin grabbed at the cat but it edged further away. "Crazy cat," Austin mumbled.

D

Children like to be able to choose what they wear and to show off their new fashion gear. This causes a lot of arguments between them and their parents over what to wear for school. Children often resent the school rules about uniform while their parents think it is important for schools to have a uniform.

Q2 **For each of the paragraphs in Q1, write the opening sentence of a paragraph that will come straight after it.**

Q3 **Copy out each of these opening sentences and then use them to complete a paragraph with three or more sentences:**

a) If you're thinking of buying a dog, you need to consider what a big responsibility it is.
b) I think a good friend has three key qualities.
c) Later that night the phone rang and her father got the bad news.
d) Surveys have shown that most Year 7 pupils share similar worries about starting at secondary school.
e) If you find someone who is unconscious, there are three simple steps you should take.

I hereby declare this sentence — open...

Each new paragraph needs to say right away what it's about (unless it's a bit of speech or something) **so that the reader knows what's going on. Otherwise they won't be able to follow it. Then he scored.**

Finding the Main Point in a Paragraph

Q1 Summarise the main point being made in each of the following paragraphs. You should write only one sentence to summarise each paragraph. *(keep it short)*

hint — stick as close as you can to what's written in the paragraph

a) Scientists have suggested more than eighty reasons to explain why dinosaurs died out on our planet. One idea is that they may have been struck by a deadly plague. Another recent suggestion is that they were wiped out when the earth was struck by a huge meteorite. Someone even suggested they were hunted into extinction by aliens.

b) In the middle of a channel of icy water, Alcatraz became a prison island for America's toughest criminals. No one could survive in the water long enough to swim to the mainland. Each corner of the prison was guarded by watchtowers equipped with guns and searchlights. There was one guard for every three prisoners. No wonder the few escape attempts all ended in failure.

c) It boasts a top speed of 130 miles per hour and accelerates from 0-60 in a hair-raising 4.1 seconds. Yet surprisingly, this car is also very economical for a car of its type, managing an average 24 miles per gallon of fuel. It certainly is a very classy performer, if you can believe the manufacturer's hype.

Q2 In this paragraph the main sentence is already underlined. Say what effect the rest of the paragraph has on it. Choose the best answer from the options below.

> "<u>Professor Zlarg had never known an attack of such ferocity on his small space rocket.</u> He heard a booming in his ears, and he thought his brain would explode. The sides of the rocket rattled and smoke poured out of the computer units. The pressure seals were cracking. Soon there would only be one defence seal left."

The other sentences help to:

a) describe the ferocity of the attack on Professor Zlarg's rocket.

b) show that defence seals are regularly to be found in the North Sea.

c) support and strengthen the main point being made.

Q3 Match the appropriate summary (parts a - d on the left) with the ideas below. Then choose <u>one</u> of these and extend it into a full paragraph.

a) Giving up smoking....

b) How hang-gliders got their name...

c) The greatest challenge of my life ...

d) Problems with English...

"They were first called this because the pilot literally hangs underneath the glider's large triangular wing."

"I like to write stories but I find spelling really difficult even with a dictionary."

"It is never too late to give up cigarettes for the sake of your health."

"The 20th June was the most difficult day that I had faced since I had started at the school."

I suggest not sitting on a paragraph then...

They say paragraphs need points. Maybe they're right. But this one doesn't.

Getting the Best Sentence Order

Q1 These are the first paragraphs of two different newspaper stories. Rewrite the paragraphs by changing the order of the sentences so the most interesting and important details come first.

a) He first realised the ladders were gone when he stepped back and slipped, sending his bucket and wash leathers plummeting 15 metres to the ground. Gary, who had to be rescued by the local fire brigade, was said to be feeling a bit down about the whole thing. A man nearly fell to his death yesterday when daring thieves made off with his set of ladders. 38 year old Gary Chamois, a professional window cleaner, had his ladders stolen from him while he was cleaning an upstairs window. Gary, a father of two, had stepped onto a ledge to reach the windows and it was at this time that the ladders were stolen.

b) Melinda is aged 20 and her mum is a hairdresser. Melinda Metaphor's new single sold more copies on the first day of release than any other single in history. Melinda is now working on her next album for release later in the year. Some dedicated fans camped all night outside record stores in order to be the first to buy.

Q2 Rewrite the following six sentences into one paragraph. Combine the sentences in the box, so that your paragraph has only **three** sentences in it. Use the linking words underneath to help.

The Ford Zippy has power steering.

The Chrysler Fantasy has computer-controlled ignition.

The Zippy uses new low-pollution fuel.

The Fantasy is powered by batteries.

The Zippy has been designed to be very economical.

The Fantasy is extremely comfortable.

whereas *although* *while*

Q3 Write the following sentences in the best order so this opening paragraph builds to a climax and then ends with an anti-climax.

It was still pitch black outside. Eventually, reluctantly I decided I had no choice — I had to get up and let the dog in. Still the howling continued. I opened my eyes. Then I heard the howl. It sent spine-tingling shivers flashing down my back. I pulled the blankets over my head but I could still hear the howling. I broke into a sweat and my teeth chattered with fear.

Order of sentences is as important of as order words...

Writing paragraphs is like telling a story or telling a joke. If the facts are in the wrong order the story won't make sense or the joke won't be funny. Think about what makes most sense and is most effective.

Varying Sentence Structure

Q1 **Rewrite these sentences so that the verb (the 'doing' word) has most emphasis:**

e.g. The car screeched round the corner at a hundred miles an hour and crashed into the fence.

Screeching round the corner at a hundred miles an hour, the car crashed into the fence.

a) I sang at the top of my voice and enjoyed my first hot bath in a week.
b) The stuntwoman leapt out of the burning plane and pulled her ripcord at the very last moment.
c) Before he was rushed to hospital, the scout leader had assured all the scouts that a sharp knife was a safe knife.

Q2 **Form these short sentences into one long complex sentence to convey the rhythm of this bus journey:**

The bus chugged out of the bus station. The bus changed gear as it climbed the hill out of the town. At the top of the hill the bus built up speed. The bus's engine began to roar. The bus went even faster. The passengers on the bus were thrown from side to side. The bus still accelerated down the hill. The driver shouted out that the brakes had failed. The driver jumped out of his cab at the last moment.

Q3 **Break the long sentences in this paragraph down into short simple sentences to convey the climber's breathlessness. To stop you getting too breathless yourself, I've started it for you.**

The tired climber grabbed hold of the rope, pulling hard on it to make sure it was secure, then he began to climb. He breathed hard because the air was thin at this height and his oxygen had run out. Slowly he lifted one foot after the other, his hands grappling for handholds as he moved incredibly slowly up the sheer rock face. His left foot slipped on a chunk of ice and he grabbed out with his right hand to find to his horror that his rope was snapping so he reached for a hold on the rock but it was too late and he fell off and out into thin air, never to be seen again.

The tired climber grabbed hold of the rope. He pulled hard on it to make sure it was secure...

Q4 **Exclamations say something surprising, exciting, urgent or awful. Write out five of the sentences in this paragraph as exclamations by adding an exclamation mark.**

It had seemed like a good idea to make mum breakfast in bed. But how it had gone wrong. The toast had burnt. The kitchen was like a battlefield. What a mess. There was jam all over the ceiling and the coffee pot lay in pieces on the floor. That would cost hundreds of pounds to put right. I only wanted to be helpful. What a mistake. The cooker was covered in flour and butter. Another mistake. I put my head in my hands. I would never try to be helpful again. Never again.

Getting Paragraphs in the Right Order

Q1 The key to success in writing is to plan your ideas into a number of paragraphs which lead from start to finish.

This story is called 'My first day at school'.
Write the letters of the paragraphs in the order in which they happened:

A. He took us to the hall for an assembly where the Head welcomed us and made some jokes no one understood, and then we went to our form room. Our teacher really confused us with timetables and school rules.

B. When the bell rang for the start of school we all had to line up in rows. Our form teacher came to collect us and showed us around the place. It didn't look too bad and a gorgeous smell drifted out of the dinner hall.

C. Before we knew it, it was break time. We ran into the playground and stuck together for safety. The rest of the day was a blur and when I got home I fell asleep in front of the television.

D. I felt better when I met my mates at the bus stop. We all looked new and felt small compared to all the big kids. They started trying to frighten us with stories about what would happen to us at the big school. We all tried to look brave. I felt sick again.

E. That morning I got up with a sick feeling inside. I didn't want any breakfast and my mum kept fussing over me. I felt a right idiot with my new bag and pencil case and my new blazer, two sizes too big.

Q2 Listed below are some of the different **types** of paragraph from the story in Q1. For each one, say what job you think it does for the story. I've done the first one for you.

a) the introduction

a) It introduces the narrator to us, and makes us interested in finding out what happens to him.

b) the conclusion

c) the second paragraph

Q3 Write a new conclusion for the story in Q1. Write one that ends unhappily, and think hard about how the final line will help the reader to get the message.

Q4 Write these paragraph starters under two headings, Introductory Starters and Concluding Starters:

a) Finally...
b) The worst which can happen is...
c) The last stage in programming the video is...
d) It all started when...
e) In conclusion, fox hunting should be banned because...
f) Teachers and pupils can never agree over school rules...

Hyenas don't have gizzards — but they do have fur...

I guess this is where I stress the importance of what order all the paragraphs should come in. BUT, to be totally honest... I couldn't give a flying pair of hyena gizzards, as it's the end of the section. ☺

Information Texts

The present tense is used to make information texts sound more up-to-date.

Q1 Some of the words in this extract need to be changed so that the whole paragraph is in the present tense. Rewrite the whole lot, changing the underlined words where necessary.

> Mountain bikes <u>were</u> becoming increasingly popular. Their design <u>made</u> them perfect for riding off-road, though in fact most mountain bike riders <u>stick</u> to tarmac. Mountain bikes <u>have</u> a strong frame, and their pedals <u>were</u> higher than ordinary pedal bikes. Mountain bikes <u>have</u> straight handlebars, and big tyres for gripping rough surfaces. To make it easier to ride on uneven ground and up steep hills, mountain bikes <u>could have</u> lots of gears.

*Information texts often use third person impersonal statements such as "**there is**" or "**it is**" instead of personal statements such as "**I**" or "**you**".*

Q2 Say which of these sentences are impersonal and which are personal statements.

a) You must check your brakes every week to ensure they are working.

b) The spacecraft was crippled by laser blasts right from the outset of the battle.

c) Pupils must record their homework in their Student Planner.

d) It is essential that the player remains calm and focused when taking the penalty in an important football match.

e) We expect all pupils to wear the correct uniform.

Q3 Use these sentence openings to help you write paragraphs for the blurb in a CD booklet.

Paragraph 1: The group Danni and the Screamers have been playing together for ......
They met when ....

Paragraph 2: They have a style which is based on .....
Fans of Danni also buy CDs by ....

Paragraph 3: Danni's real name is .....
As well as the band, the Screamers spend their spare time ....

Paragraph 4: The band's most loyal fans are ....

Q4 Information texts usually give examples. Rewrite each of these paragraphs, adding an example in each of the spaces.

a) Secondary schools could make lessons more enjoyable for pupils in three main ways. For example they could ..*e.g.*.. . Another way that teachers could encourage pupils to enjoy lessons is ..*e.g.*.. . Finally, pupils would enjoy their lessons more if ..*e.g.*.. .

b) Before families buy a dog they should consider three main things. Firstly, parents should ..*e.g.*.. . Secondly, it is vital that the children ..*e.g.*.. . A third consideration is ..*e.g.*.. .

Information texts — it's all a matter of fact...

Remember to <u>organise</u> your information into <u>logical chunks</u> and <u>use examples</u> to explain your points. Whatever you do, <u>don't get distracted</u> and — oooh is that chocolate?

Recount Texts

'Recount' means to tell a story of something that has happened in the past. Recount texts are usually written in the past tense.

Q1 Rewrite this paragraph, changing the underlined verbs into the past tense.

"You won't believe this but I am late for school because of the dog. I take her to the park first thing this morning and she runs after a rabbit then she gets distracted and chases the paperboy who is crossing the road outside the park. Before I can catch up with her she has forgotten the paperboy and is chasing the number 11 bus. When the bus opens its doors, she only jumps on board and, to my horror, the bus drives off."

Q2 Write another paragraph that finishes off this story.
Make sure you keep all the verbs in the past tense.

Non-fiction stories are usually written in chronological order — in other words, in the same order as the events happened.

Q3 What order should these paragraphs be in so that the story is in chronological order?

a) When it was all over and I was walking back home, I remember thinking that when the next eclipse happens I'll be eighty-eight years old and I'll need a walking stick, not a mountain bike, to help me get around.

b) A small crowd gathered and I joined them to stare into the sky. Birds were singing. Slowly the moon's face crept across the sun, shutting out its rays.

c) Very very slowly, the sun disappeared. Day turned to night and it grew colder as the sun disappeared totally. There was almost complete darkness except for a ring of light around the moon.

d) The eclipse was going to occur at dawn. My sister and I put on warm clothing and trudged up to the hilltop. Normally we weren't allowed to go there on our own but today was going to be special. We were dead excited.

Q4 Use 'time link' words from the box to fill the gaps in these sentences. Use each word once.

during	as soon as	later on	while	until	after

a) The family car broke down .... the worst rainstorm in history.

b) The pilot pulled the pararchute cord .... he leapt out of the plane.

c) The burglar took the opportunity to break into the house .... they were away on their holidays.

d) We lit the bonfire and, ... , enjoyed burnt sausages as fireworks burst into gorgeous colours all around us.

e) They waited in utter silence .... the wood fell dark and the shadows lengthened in the courtyard of the wizard's castle.

f) .... three days they ran out of food and there was only sufficient water for another day.

There's usually more than one OK answer, but remember you can only use each one once.

Writing about insomnia — recounting sheep...

Recount texts tell you what's happened — make sure your verbs are in the past tense and that everything happens in the right order — you don't want to be dancing before the party's started...

Explanation Texts

Explanations tell us how things work, why things happen or what people think. They are written in the present tense.

Q1 a) Change the verbs in this explanation into the present tense.

> *"Wordprocessors in computers checked the spelling of the document. Most also checked the grammar too. If they did not recognise a word they offered the user a list of alternatives. Some wordprocessors checked spelling as you typed. In Word, odd words were underlined in red."*

b) Explain how another modern electrical device works, making sure you keep all the verbs in the present tense.

Q2 Explanations often use impersonal statements as well as personal ones. Sort these explanations into impersonal and personal statements.

a) You can use a PC for all kinds of things such as wordprocessing, handling images and playing games.
b) If you will listen, I will explain to you exactly how the vase got broken and the best carpet ruined.
c) The PC can be used for all kinds of activities such as wordprocessing, handling images and data.
d) There are several explanations as to how the vase was smashed and the expensive new carpet was spoiled.

Q3 Choose the best word from the box to link the ideas in these explanations.

so	therefore	then	in order that	as a result	because

a) Monopoly is a game about making money, ... the winner is the person who finishes with most cash left.
b) You must not walk on the floor for twenty-four hours after laying the tiles .... the adhesive will not have set properly.
c) The joystick option has been added .... that players can control the cars more effectively.
d) The game can get very physical and .... it is better played outdoors.
e) Suddenly one of them barged past us and .... my father was knocked off his bike.
f) You need to put the foundation blocks there, ... lay the coloured bricks on top.

This page could explain the hind legs off a donkey...

Remember — you should have got your verbs in the right tense — or no one will know what was going on. It all gets very confusing and they will have stopped reading what you're about to write.

Instruction Texts

*Instruction texts tell us how to do something and what to do to get things done. They use **imperatives,** or commands, to tell you to do something. e.g. "**Turn** left at the traffic lights."*

Q1 Re-write these sentences as imperatives.

a) You have to be home before midnight.
b) You should light the blue touch-paper and then you should stand well back.
c) You have to hand in your homework before Friday.
d) You must overpower the Dark Lord and then rescue the princess in the tower.
e) You must walk the dog before you leave for school.
f) You should read all the instructions before starting to glue components together.
g) You must not press the red button because it will launch the incredible green slime missile straight into the school hall.

Simon was beginning to wish he'd looked at the instructions before he started.

Q2 Instruction texts get the steps in the best order for doing something. Put these instructions in the right order.

a) Pour the beans on the toast. Butter the toast. Open the can of beans. Empty the beans into the saucepan. Slice the bread and put it in the toaster. Turn the cooker on. Check with an adult that it is safe for you to make lunch. Take out a plate and cutlery.

b) Let your bike dry properly before putting it back in the shed. Put in one capful of detergent. Clean all the surfaces thoroughly with the soapy water. Stand your bike in the yard. Fill a bucket half full of hot water. Stir the water well with the sponge to dissolve the soap fully. Wheel your bike out of the shed. Get a fresh bucket of cold water and use it to rinse the bike.

Q3 Write your own article for a magazine, giving a simple explanation of how to do something. Choose from this list if you're stuck for ideas.

— how to find music on the internet
— how to play a sport
— how to prepare for that all-important school disco
— how to care for a pet
— how to get from your house to school
— how to make a simple snack

Homework instruction no.1: Turn the TV on... (no, wait...)

Instruction writing does exactly what it says on the tin. Literally. You're giving a set of instructions — they'll be completely useless if you get bits in the wrong order or miss out something important.

Persuasion Texts

Persuasion is when you use words to not only put across your point of view but also to get your reader to accept your views and, if possible, agree with them.

Q1 Write out each of the different phrases which the writer uses to show they are sorry in this passage.

"I really am sorry, sir, about that broken window. I do regret kicking that ball straight through your window. I know it was daft to be playing football right under the head teacher's window, especially after all the warnings. I wish I could find some way to apologise for that. I can only promise you that it will not happen again. I really really mean that. I will never kick that ball again — unless you're prepared to return it, that is."

Q2 Put your point of view across by showing you believe in it. Complete these sentence stems with some of your own ideas.

a) You've got to believe me when I say ......
b) It seems to me quite obvious that .....
c) I truly believe that .....
d) It seems to me .....
e) No sane person could argue against the idea that.....

Persuasive writing contains (i) an opinion, (ii) an example, (iii) a reason for the example.

Q3 Copy out both of the following passages. For each one, underline and label the parts which are opinions, examples and reasons.

a) *I really don't agree with foxhunting. I think it's cruel and barbaric. I think this because of the immense suffering that the innocent foxes are subjected to. I heard of one hunt which took 4 1/2 hours to finish, at which point the fox was ripped to pieces by hounds. I think it's utterly inhumane and should be stopped.*

b) *I think television's great because you can get more up-to-date information than you can from books. Just last night I was watching a documentary about pollution that was only filmed last month. I disagree with people who say that telly rots the brain. I think they're just being narrow-minded.*

Go on — go on, go on, go on, go on, go on, go on...

In persuasive texts you're trying to get the reader to believe or agree with your views. It helps to make your opinions more believable if you back them up with lots of examples. No really it does...

Discursive Writing

Discursive writing means writing about different points of view.

Q1 For each of these examples, use the 'signpost' phrases to write down a second view which contradicts the idea in the first sentence. I've done the first one for you.

a) Some people think that fox-hunting is cruel. Foxes kill chickens, which is also cruel.

However, in my opinion...

Some people think that fox-hunting is cruel.
However, in my opinion, foxes killing chickens is cruel

b) King Harold had a lot of bad luck as he raced down to face the Norman invasion. William the Conqueror was better organised and more determined.

On the other hand...

c) Watching too much television stops children reading. Many books only become popular with young readers because they are televised.

Another point of view is that...

d) School uniform is a good advertisement for the school. School kids who wear raggedy ties, untucked shirts and who misbehave on the high street at lunch time only get the school a bad name.

But you can also argue that...

e) If more people cycled to work all year round, there would be less pollution and so people would be healthier. There would inevitably be a rise in accidents with cars, and some riders would be injured for life.

However, some people would also argue that...

Q2 Write out each of these sentences and underline the words which show that the writer is giving their view or opinion.

a) It seems to me that older people see all teenagers as wild, selfish, noisy animals.
b) Most sci-fi films present aliens as the enemy of mankind but in my opinion it is just as likely that we will be able to live in peace with alien life forms.
c) I really don't agree with people who think that Christmas is all about how much you can spend buying presents and having a good time.
d) I think that eventually scientists will find a drug which will make parents good-humoured and patient, all year round, with their children, so that all kids will get a hundred per cent rise in pocket money every month.

Q3 Use the 'signpost' phrases in Q1 to write your own pairs of sentences which put contradictory ideas for and against a controversial topic.

Who will rid me of dis curse of writing...

Discursive writing involves looking at a topic from all angles. You need to talk about your own ideas and also contradictory ones — even though you don't agree with them. Then again, you might agree with them. Or not. Or maybe yes. In fact, I could discuss this for ages and zzzzzzzzzzzzzz...

Using the Right Styles

Q1 **You write differently in each school subject because you're writing for different reasons. Match each of these types of writing to the correct example.**

a) tell your reader the facts about an event
b) present arguments for and against a particular issue
c) describe how something works
d) describe how to do something through a series of logical steps
e) put forward a particular point of view, backed up with information/statistics
f) present arguments and information from differing points of view before giving your own conclusion
g) tell your reader about a product such as a book, film or CD and give your opinion about how good it is

i) Your English teacher asks you to write an essay with arguments for and against experiments on animals.
ii) Your history teacher asks you to write down what happened at the Battle of Hastings.
iii) Your Science teacher asks you to write about an experiment you performed to test if boys' brains were bigger than girls'.
iv) Your technology teacher asks you to describe how a tin-opener works.
v) Your English teacher asks you to write an advertisement for a pair of trainers which enable the wearer to run faster than a speeding bullet.
vi) Your English teacher asks you to write about a film you have enjoyed watching.
vii) Your RE teacher asks you to write about whether you can ever justify committing a crime.

Q2 **Match each of these examples with the correct type of writing in a) to g) from Q1.**

i) Gary held the test tube while I poured the salt into the hot water and we watched to see how much salt we could dissolve in it.
ii) There are loads of opinions over whether the Loch Ness monster actually exists. In this essay I am going to look at the main arguments for and against, and next weekend Gary and I are going to go and look for ourselves.
iii) The computer is an incredible machine made up of a monitor or TV screen, a processor which does the 'thinking' and a hard disc which is the mechanical brain's memory bank.
iv) Liverpool are great. They're the best football team in the world. They've won 8 out of their last 10 games and they haven't conceded a goal for 6 games.

Get the style right — steer well clear of that '80s fringe...

Stlye (can't even type it — doesn't bode well...). **Hmm. Style** (that's better). **Before you write anything on the page, write down** (on your hand maybe) **what style you're going to write in. Then stick to it.**

Formal and Informal

Q1 Each expression (1 - 4) has a formal and informal version. Draw two columns headed 'Formal' and 'Informal' and write each expression in the correct column.

❶
a) How do you do?
b) Wotcher, mate.

❷
c) There were, like, millions of people in the shop.
d) The department store was very crowded.

❸
e) I am afraid I do not know.
f) I dunno, do I?

❹
g) I wonder if you could help me?
h) Give us a hand.

Q2 Now, make up four of your own pairs and add them to the table.

When you know someone personally you can speak to them informally. If you don't — probably better to be formal.

Q3 Add these people to the table. Put them in the 'formal' or 'informal' columns to show how you should speak to them.

a) your brother
b) your head teacher
c) a visiting politician
d) your best friend

Q4 If you are in situations where you have to be on best behaviour, you might have to be formal. Write the letter of each example and then write the number of the situation which matches it.

Examples:

a) when large groups hear you speak
b) when what you say is being judged or assessed
c) when you talk to someone with more authority than you

Situations:

i) you are giving evidence in court
ii) you are talking to the Head Teacher
iii) you are giving a talk in assembly

Q5 Now write down two more examples for categories a), b) and c) in Q4.

Q6 Writing is the same as speaking — we can be formal or informal. Copy out these bits of letters and write 'Formal' or 'Informal' beside them.

a) Two pints of skimmed tomorrow — none for rest of week — on holiday!
b) I would like to say that I strongly disagree with the article published on Monday claiming a decrease in quality of educational publishing.
c) I would like to invite you to interview on 4th of July at our head office.
d) I believe some of my family emigrated to your part of America in the late nineteenth century and I would be delighted if you could provide any background information on the people of the town around 1880.
e) I love my new secondary school but I miss you and all the other teachers in Hazbin Primary, well, most of them!
f) Mandy and Jesmina both wore the same dress —
I wish you could have been there to see their faces!

Keeping Up the Standard

Standard English is the writing or speaking of English without local words, phrases or slang. This means that English speakers everywhere can understand you.

Q1 Match each informal expression with the appropriate standard English phrase.

Informal (or colloquial) English:	**Standard English:**
a) The article is all about "Eng-er-land!"	It was unpopular.
b) We didn't half laugh.	It amused us.
c) The dog was down the street in a flash.	It looks at patriotism.
d) Everyone thinks it's a rubbish idea.	It ran very quickly.

Q2 Below are sentences from an essay about Shakespeare. Rewrite each sentence in standard English. Use words and phrases from the box to help you.

prevent	many people	actor
also	suffered from	the theatres were
fortunately for him	children	it is believed that
playwright	during his lifetime	

a) When he was around, loads of people died young.
b) Masses of people had the plague too.
c) Sometimes they closed theatres to stop the plague spreading.
d) He never got it, though.
e) As well as writing plays, he was in them, they think.

Q3 Write out the following sentences and underline the non-standard English words in them.

a) About their defeat, the England manager would only say he was gutted.
b) The film tracks his relationship with his girlfriend and ends when she dumps him.
c) Looking ahead to the weekend, a cold front moving in from the west means it will rain cats and dogs on Saturday.
d) When Duncan asked his boss for the day off he was told to get lost.
e) The plumber told Mrs. Gladdings that her dishwasher had conked out.
f) The ladies met for a good old chinwag in the tearooms every Tuesday.

Q4 Rewrite the examples above, replacing the underlined parts with standard English phrases.

Q5 Write a letter of complaint to a local cinema manager.
Use the notes below to write a formal letter using standard English.

Asked for a small popcorn and was given something the size of a bucket!

Noisy children at the front — couldn't hear properly

Rubbish under seat when I arrived — health and safety hazard

Very annoyed by last visit

Never using your cinema again unless refund is given...

'Old yer 'orses — don't get in a two an' eight...

You can use slang with your mates. In fact accents and slang are colourful and interesting. BUT you've got to turn on your standard English when you need it, like in essays and exams.

The Changing Language

Q1 **For examples a) to f) write either 'Older text' or 'Modern text'.**

a) Little Abraham was aroused from his deep sleep in a corner of the same apartment, and made to put on his clothes while still mentally in the other world. Meanwhile Tess had hastily dressed herself; and the twain, lighting a lantern, went out to the stable.

b) "It's no good," sighed Inspector Helix, rubbing the stubble that had grown in the two days since he had shaved, then sitting back and loosening his tie. "If the killer is out there, he's covered his tracks too well for us to find him. We might never trace him."

c) They never travelled together — it was company policy. The recipe was known only by these two men. If a plane went down with them on it, the recipe for the popular cereal would be lost forever — and that was just too awful for the Board of Directors to contemplate.

d) The story held us, round the fire, sufficiently breathless, but, except the obvious remark that it was gruesome, as, on Christmas eve in an old house, a strange tale should essentially be, I remember no comment uttered till somebody happened to say that it was the only case he had met in which such a visitation had fallen on a child.

e) He gave her to understand that Frank admired her extremely — thought her very beautiful and very charming; and with so much to be said for him altogether, she found she must not judge him harshly.

f) The reality of the situation — lost, broke and with no one to turn to — hit Derry hard. He had to think — and think fast.

Q2 **How could you tell which texts were older? Write true or false for each of the following:**

a) Older texts sometimes have words we don't use any more.

b) Modern texts are shorter.

c) Modern texts tend to sound simpler.

d) Older texts tend to sound more formal.

e) Modern texts describe things in more detail.

f) Older texts often have complex sentence structures.

Q3 **Complete the following tasks using one of the extracts you decided was an older text in Q1.**

a) Underline any old-fashioned words.

b) Choose one and look up its definition in a dictionary. Write this out.

c) Choose one sentence from an older text that you could rewrite in a modern style. Write it out, replacing words, phrases or punctuation to make the sentence structure simpler.

They* were very wordy† in the past *(now we have the footnote)...*

What's important is that you get used to thinking about how different authors use language, and why they do it. There's a huge difference between older and modern language — useful, eh?

* 'They' refers to all authors of any sex or ethnic origin and the author accepts no responsibilty for any offence caused to anyone by this term.

† The word,'wordy' is a registered trademark. Any use of this word constitutes breach of copyright under section 452 of the copyright law. Honest.

Finding Out

Q1 For each piece of information, write down the resource from the box where it might be found. Some options may be used more than once.

a) shops that sell the latest hi-fi speakers
b) the detailed history of the sport of greyhound racing
c) the definition of a word
d) current affairs in the UK
e) how to spell a word in the plural
f) last night's football results
g) words similar in meaning to "shiver"

dictionary	website	thesaurus
encyclopaedia	specialist magazine	newspaper

Q2 You have to find out what 30 degrees Celsius is in degrees Fahrenheit. You have found an encyclopaedia. Write out the steps to finding the answer in the right order.

a) skim-read the description of the history of the two measurements
b) write down the answer: 86
c) scan down the lists of numbers until you find '30' in the Celsius column
d) check the key words, arranged alphabetically at the top corners of each page, until you find the page with "Celsius"
e) read across carefully to the column with 'Fahrenheit'
f) follow the page reference to find the quick conversion table

Q3 Make a table with two columns headed 'Glossary' and 'Contents'. Copy the extracts from books below into the correct columns.

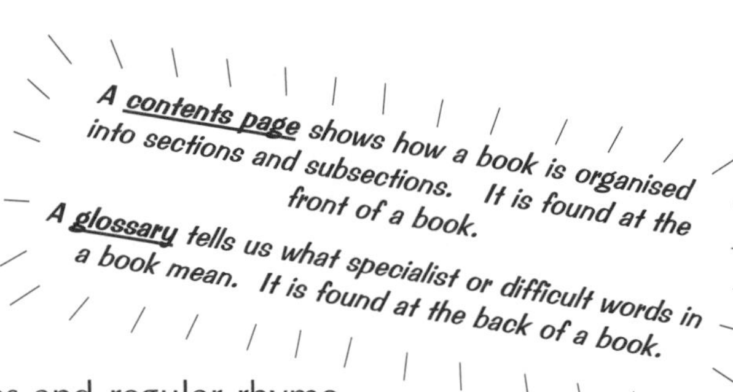

a) Fathom: 1.83 metres
b) Winter plants and how to nourish them.
c) 1917 — The Russian Revolution
d) limerick: short humorous poem of five lines and regular rhyme
e) Drawing Still Life
f) Stage left: to the left of an actor on stage facing the audience
g) The Largest Countries in the World
h) Pula: unit of currency in Botswana

Q4 Put the following in order to show how you would use Internet searches to answer the question "Which two teams played the opening game of the World Cup in France, 1998?"

a) open the website
b) call up a search engine
c) scan the home page for key words and useful links
d) enter 'World Cup 1998'
e) write down the answer: Brazil v Scotland
f) skim through the sites until you find an official one that is in English
g) click on a hotlink to 'Opening Game'
h) scan the page for the section on the first game.

Different Ways of Reading

Q1 These are different ways of reading. Write the words out in order from the most thorough to the quickest. You can check a dictionary for any meanings you are unsure of.

a) scan
b) skim-read
c) check
d) edit

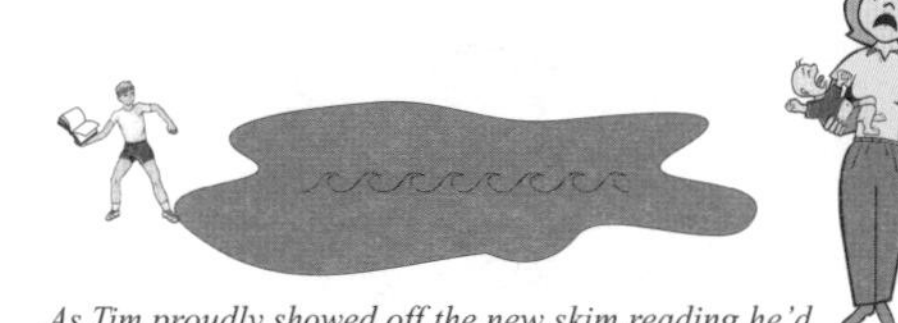

As Tim proudly showed off the new skim reading he'd learnt at school he wondered why his mum started to slowly sob.

Q2 Copy out the sentences below and write which of the four words from Q1 match the activity described.

a) Brian asked Jenny whether her figures were correct. She decided to go back and look them up again, just to be sure.
b) Claire quickly read through the adverts, looking for the one she had paid to have printed in this week's paper.
c) Barry picked up the seventy-five-page report. He would quickly read it to get the general idea of its findings.
d) The essay was over its word limit. Jade read it through again, trying to decide which bits really had to stay in.

Q3 Skim-read this passage. Write down the name of Gerald's aunt and explain her complaint in your own words.

> Gerald hated this time of year. As soon as the Christmas tree was up, his entire family seemed to think they could cram themselves into the front room and guzzle all the mulled wine and mince pies their fat faces could hold. Muriel, his mother, was worn out by the end of each evening. Once, when her sister, Madeleine, had complained the pies were running out, he had found her preparing to bake another batch in the kitchen.

Q4 Scan this passage for three types of music and write them down.

> According to Jules, the only music worth hearing was reggae. Then Sam introduced her to garage. She thought she might have to admit that it was good music too. It wasn't like the country stuff her dad kept insisting she listen to, or the soft rock her mum liked. This music was edgy with something new to say.

Q5 Read this passage, checking for mistakes. Then write it out correctly.

> Fourteen busses were out of commission on Saturday last week but only on of them was still off the road the fllowing day

Reading — isn't that near Guildford...?

To answer simple questions you can often skim through and look for relevant bits. Other times you might need to read slowly and carefully — selecting the best type of reading can save lots of time.

Presenting Your Information

Q1 Write down which of these are ways to present information:

a) a paragraph
b) a pie chart
c) a graph
d) a sketch
e) a photograph
f) a list
g) a table
h) a web page

Q2 Write down the best way of presenting each of these examples (choose from those given in Q1). Write an explanation of each choice.

a) The increases and decreases in your savings account over the last five years.
b) The grades everyone in the class got in their last two end-of-year exams.
c) An explanation of the changes that occurred after the last general election.
d) The people you want to invite to your birthday party.
e) The way people now look, having lived in the refugee camp for five weeks.
f) The way you'd want your bedroom to look if you got the chance to decorate it.
g) Information about your school that should be accessible to as many people as possible.
h) The results of a survey for PSHE about the proportion of your class in favour of or against the current amount of homework they receive.

Q3 Below are three ways of presenting the same information about the survey described in Q2 h). Look at the information and answer the questions which follow:

① When asked whether the current back-breaking workload that we are forced to do for homework is satisfactory or whether it should be cut to more manageable levels, everyone in the class had an opinion. The vast majority were overwhelmingly in favour of a substantial cut in hours spent doing homework.

②

Name	Satisfactory	Unsatisfactory
Jed		yes
Martin		yes
Dianna		yes
Yvonne		yes
Simon	yes	

③

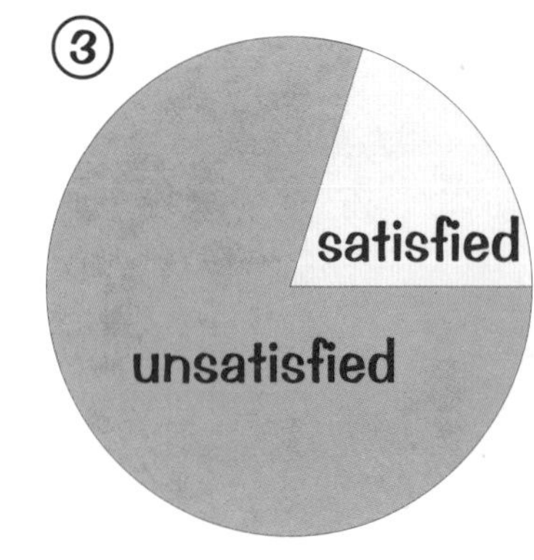

Give reasons for each of your answers:

a) If you were in favour of cutting the amount of homework, which method of showing the results appears to support your view most strongly (1, 2 or 3)?
b) Which method would be most likely to persuade other members of the class (who weren't included in the first survey) into agreeing with you?
c) Which method shows that the survey was too small to indicate significant support?

Making Notes

Q1 True or false? Copy out the true statements from below.

a) Notes are always written in full sentences.
b) Notes save us time.
c) Sometimes notes can help organise our plans for writing.
d) Notes can be prompts representing more complex ideas or information.
e) Notes are only written in symbols called 'shorthand'.

Q2 Say which of the situations below are good examples of when to make notes.

a) Your teacher is introducing a new subject in class and is talking too fast for you to write down everything she says.
b) You are asked to prepare a speech for a class debate.
c) You are in an exam and want to make sure you have thought through all your points before you start writing.
d) You are comparing the prices of different models in three or four shops before deciding which new sound system to buy.
e) You are writing down a recipe for a friend.

Q3 Read all the examples below and copy out those which **are** examples of notes.

a) reasons FOR = cheaper, faster, more popular, more convenient
b) Then, attach the red wire to the socket marked "POWER".
c) Lived in London all life, wrote poems and illustrated them.
d) Anderson, signed treaty, 1845 - only lasted a year
e) Sift the flour, then fold in the softened butter by hand.
f) Intro = idea of sexism still around; first paragraph = number of women in top executive jobs much smaller than the number of men.

Q4 The paragraph below is from a history book. A student made some notes on the paragraph. Some of the notes are better than others. Copy out the notes which you think are good.

> The chief imports into Archangel, in north-west Russia throughout the sixteenth century were gold and silver, lace of many kinds, dyes such as cochineal and indigo, wine, brandy and other spirits. Its greatest export goods were tar and cod, earning considerable revenue from cities across Russia and other northern countries.

a) Archangel is in north-west Russia.
b) Sixteenth century imports were gold and silver and many kinds of lace
c) Other imports were dyes like cochineal and indigo
d) c16th Archangel: main imports = precious metals, laces, dyes and alcohol
e) Earned money from exporting tar and cod across Europe

You and I could make beautiful notes together...

Notes: key points, abbrev., symbols — save time — make sure clear...
Erm — nuff said...

Useful Information

Q1 For each of the search tasks below, say which source is most relevant to the task set.

a) **Task** Find out all you can about King Christian of Denmark.

Sources
i) The Royal Families of Europe Through the Ages
ii) King Christian's Love of Music
iii) King Christian of Denmark - A Life

Danish Royal Cutlery

b) **Task** Find out who Cardiff City beat to win the FA Cup in 1927.

Sources
i) FA Cup Winners 1945 to the present day.
ii) FA Cup Winners of the Twentieth Century
iii) Cardiff City's Golden Year — The Story of the 1927 Cup Winners' Road to Victory

c) **Task** What are the opening times of the London Eye?

Sources
i) London Tourist Information — What's On Today
ii) The London Eye: Weekly Schedule
iii) Designing the London Eye

Q2 In Q1 which two, of all the sources, are irrelevant to the task?

Q3 Relevant sources quickly give you direct answers. For each task in Q1, write out the sources in order from most valuable to least valuable.

Q4 It's important to say where you get your information from. Write out the acknowledged sources below (a, b & c), and next to them write what type of acknowledgement it is. (The types are written in the grey box.)

footnote or reference	acknowledging a quote	bibliography

a) 20% of children died before they reached the age of one that year[1].
1. Survey by Brackish and Tainted Waterworks Ltd, 1877.

b) *Sponges and Their Natural Habitats*, Dr A. Scrubb, (CGP Ltd, 2001)

c) Pizzas were suddenly the wonder food of America. "Everyone in New York was going into the pizza trade — men made their fortunes within a year or two." (Mr. P. Hut in *The New York Times*, 14th June, 1965).

Q5 Each type of acknowledgement should be put in a different place. For each location (a–c) write the type of ackowledgement which would be put there. Use the types in the grey box in Q4 again.

a) Include them in the main text along with your writing, but separate them with brackets.
b) Include them at the foot of the page or the end of the chapter.
c) Include them at the very end of the project along with other books you read or made use of to complete the work.

Making Meaning from Texts

Q1 For each of the definitions below write down the correct word from the grey box.

empathising	predicting	relating to your own experience	visualising

a) using your imagination to turn the words on a page into a picture in your head
b) trying to guess what happens next, or what happens at the end
c) trying to imagine how it must feel to experience what is being described in a text
d) thinking of something similar to the experience in the text that has happened to you

Q2 Write the technique (from the grey box above) which would be most appropriate for each example:

a) Eleanor searched her bag for the third time, the panic that she was feeling starting to show on her face. She had been sure her purse was safe in the pocket where she usually put it — why was it not there now?

b) The eagle climbed above the craggy edges of his mountain home and beat his strong wings to take him even higher. As he rose, he could feel the battling air currents around him, some warm and appealing, others chillingly cold. He needed to find a warm current to carry him closer to the thin white clouds above him.

c) Razcallion darted down a narrow alley, empty but for himself and his pursuer. He reached the end and thought he had made some ground. Where now? Right, to the busy marketplace or left, to the deserted river bank?

Q3 Write in your own words what meanings are being implied in the following examples. Focus on what the writer wants to tell us about a character. Use some of the words in the box to help.

poor	ill	guilty	greedy	cruel	angry

a) John stormed from the room and slammed the door behind him.
b) As the teacher stared accusingly, Martha shuffled uncomfortably.
c) "In the months since the epidemic hit our town, you have worked without stopping to heal our sick, Dr Hale. How *do* you do it?" asked Hunter.
The doctor, pale as death, gave a half-defeated sigh and swallowed to stifle the tickle in his throat, before summoning some energy to answer.
d) "*I'm* in charge," came her vicious little voice. "So, you have to follow *my* rules."

Q4 Write out the examples from Q3 and underline the words which helped to tell you what the implied meanings were.

You've got to read — between the lines...

Understanding a book isn't just about reading the words. Writers often stick in hidden meanings and extra little details that you might miss if you're not completely 'into' it. So go for it — lose yourself in the book and you'll get much much more from it. Here endeth the lesson according to CGP...

Reading a Whole Text for Meaning

Q1 Read these examples. For each one write down the number of the sentence in the box which gives the main points of the example.

a) The new manager came into the team like a whirlwind, replacing three key players and two backroom staff. Joe Wilmotts, the club's star striker, complained that the team's winning form might be disrupted.
b) Although the school has been low in the league tables for the last three years, the head teacher, Ronnie McDonny, says that new government funding initiatives could make that a thing of the past.
c) Some people say that animals have rights. Some people say the rainforests must be saved. We say President Candoo's ten-year reign of terror in Fritland must end.
d) As fighting enters its fourth day, conditions for civilians are deteriorating. Roads into to the city have been shut since Wednesday. There has been no water since Friday. Today we ask how long the people can continue to survive this level of bombardment.

Main points:

i)	Things are getting much worse.	(iii)	Things will be getting better.
ii)	Some ideas should be challenged.	(iv)	Things should not be changed.

Q2 The following texts have sequences or patterns. Look at the box below and write down the numbers of the patterns which match each text (some may match more than one pattern).

a) Elephant pulled, and Rhino pulled, and Hippo pulled, and Lion pulled, and Hyena pulled, and Cat pulled, and Mouse pulled. They all pulled together but they could not pull Giraffe out of the toilet.
b) For three hours Sonia walked the road out of the city. In the first hour she saw nothing unusual. The second hour, she noticed that there were fewer people. By the middle of the third hour, she saw she was entirely alone upon the highroad.
c) "Forget about what it was like when you were a kid, Dad!" cried Martin. "You played football, ate boiled sweets and swapped marbles. It's not like that now. We play computer games, eat chocolate bars and swap mobile numbers! How could you understand?"
d) In 'Meet the band', we say hi to 'Dex', the South London outfit who are big in the charts this week. Dex is Dale (19), Roxie (18), Delilah (17) and Li'l Zed (16). Roxie went to school with Delilah and they formed the basis of Dex. Auditions turned up Dale and, once the group had a record contract, their manager advised them to fill out their sound with a fourth voice. And that's where Li'l Zed came in.

Patterns:

i)	chronological order	iii)	past to present
ii)	increasing/decreasing size		

Look for Patterns and Sequences and Sequences and Sequences and Sequences

When you're reading a text look out for the main points and any patterns or sequences. It'll help you not only understand the writing, but also look at any effects the writer is trying to create.

Reading for Meaning

Q1 For each example (a–d) write the number of the view they are expressing:

a) Better health care will cost money, and we think it is worth it.
b) The smell coming from the dog was enough to make your toes curl.
c) This ridiculous scheme will benefit nobody and cost a fortune.
d) Her perfume was intoxicating.

Views:

i)	it is a good idea	iii)	it is a bad smell
ii)	it is a bad idea	iv)	it is a good smell

Q2 Sometimes writers express opinions which are not their own. Write out the following example and underline the bit which you think are NOT the writer's views.

The banning of mobile phones in school must go ahead if children are to achieve their full potential. Of course, some say that children are safer if they have a phone to keep in touch with home, but clearly, when more and more children are being attacked for the phones they carry, that argument is not valid.

Q3 The extract below is taken from an article about an archaeological discovery. Read through it and answer the questions below.

Slap Happens

Noted archaeologist Dr Happenslap rejoiced in his recent discovery of an ancient, well-preserved donkey. The reason for his feelings of elation however, was the observation that the donkey had a horn growing from its forehead, prompting a worldwide meeting of scientists and biologists to debate the possibility that Dr Happenslap had discovered the world's first and only unicorn.

The conclusion finally reached in the meeting was that what Dr Happenslap had discovered was, in fact, a unidonkey. "It's the biggest load of old frogswallop I've ever heard in my whole life," said leading genetic theorist Dr Banana. Relying on his position of power, Dr Banana has downplayed the potential importance of Happenslap's discovery from the start.

Unfortunately, the remains of the unidonkey have since been stolen, preventing any further research. Dr Happenslap has since resigned from his job as he is totally distraught. However, at least the theft of the unidonkey's remains has saved the scientist from possible further humiliation, as the glorious unidonkey could have turned out to be nothing more than a plain old ass.

a) What does Dr Banana think about the discovery?
b) What does Dr Happenslap think about his discovery (before it's stolen)?
c) How does Dr Happenslap feel after the theft?
d) What do you think the writer feels about the whole thing?

Hint — think about the tone the article is written in — and look at the last sentence.

The meaning of life is — not getting caught...

There's often a difference between what writers think and what the people they write about think. Like now. I think anyone who can call a donkey a unidonkey must be a sandwich short of a picnic...

Reading Media Texts for Meaning

Q1 Match each audience in right-hand box to the correct media text in the left-hand box:

a) The Financial Chronicle
b) J-18
c) Trout Weekly
d) The Premiership

i) teenage girls
ii) fishing fans
iii) football fans
iv) business people

Q2 Make a table with two columns: "Older People" and "Younger People". Copy these examples into the correct column to show who the adverts are most likely to be aimed at.

a) book club membership
b) charity donations to third world countries
c) mobile phone ring tones
d) disposable 'party' cameras
e) trainers
f) denture cream

Q3 Copy out the following statements and write "True" or "False" beside them.

a) Adverts for expensive aftershave are mainly aimed at male wage-earners aged twenty and up.
b) Adverts for fizzy drinks are mainly aimed at French policemen.
c) Adverts for chewing gum are mainly aimed at teachers.
d) Adverts for nappies are mainly aimed at parents of very young children.

Q4 Write down a suggested target audience for any false statements in Q3.

Q5 For each advert extract below, write 1, 2 or 3 to show the age group you think they are aimed at.

1 = below 11 years old
2 = between 11 and 17 years old
3 = above 17 years old

a) They won't listen if you ask them nicely — so *tell* them you gotta have one!
b) Because you know what's best for your little ones.
c) Bradon Financial Services. Let us help you to meet your targets — whatever they are.
d) Daisy the Puppy-Dog — she'd just love you to own her!
e) With seven different colours, there's a whole rainbow for you to play with!
f) And they're fun to share — now you know the secret of true popularity.

Q6 Use categories 1, 2 and 3 from Q5, and write down two more of your own for each one using current TV advertising slogans.

Page 54 — Just do it...✔

Advertising is a massive industry which spends ages working out what sort of adverts appeal to what audience, otherwise they'd end up with babies buying pensions and adults in nappies — crazy.

Reading Media Texts for Meaning

Q1 The images used in media texts also have to be 'read'. Write your own explanation of what these still images might mean:

a) A holiday company shows a photo in colour of a silver beach, empty apart from a young couple in swimsuits, walking away from the camera through the shallows, holding hands.
b) A frozen food manufacturer shows a colour close-up of a crisp green apple with three beads of dew glinting on it.
c) An insurance company shows a colour picture of a peacefully sleeping baby.
d) An advert for a dog's home includes a black and white photo of a small, thin dog sitting in front of an empty food bowl.

Q2 Media texts often also use music and sounds to enhance their image. Copy out these sound tracks and write the letter of the image from Q1 to which it is most suited:

a) outdoor sounds, in particular a bit of birdsong
b) a music-box playing a lullaby tune
c) a single violin playing a sad song
d) a single violing playing a romantic song

Q3 Different sounds bring different meanings. Each sound in Q2 (a–d) now has another sound added to it. Explain how these sounds bring new meaning, to add to those given in Q2.

a) the sound of biting into a crispy apple
b) a reassuring-sounding man explaining in a soothing voice about the insurance
c) the sound of a dog whining and scratching to be let out
d) a steel band playing a lively tune

Q4 Copy out the statements below which are true.

a) Bright colours usually mean positive or cheerful ideas.
b) Loud music suggests peace and tranquility.
c) Slow motion can be used to give emphasis to particular movements or expressions.
d) Sudden noises or changes in volume of the sound can grab the audience's attention.
e) Big writing is easier to ignore than small writing.
f) Choosing colours that have neutral tones helps to create a calm image.
g) Using current chart music will appeal more to teenagers than adults.
h) Web pages that have games, questionnaires or places for visitor feedback will keep visitors more interested and at the site for longer than ones which have none of these things.

What's read and all over — yep, its Section Six...

Gone are the days when reading just meant grunting vowel and consonant sounds until you formed a word. Now there are different types of reading, different types of books, media texts, and all manner of newfangled jiggery-pokery. But remember, whatever form of reading you're doing, the trick is to understand the main points and then start thinking about how to interpret what the writer's done and how they've done it. You've done a ton of reading already — so I'll stop now.

Create an Interesting Background

Q1 In stories, weather can reflect feelings. Match each of these situations with the weather that you would most expect to go with them (especially in corny films):

a) a funeral
b) a traditional Christmas scene
c) someone walking outside, feeling sad
d) someone walking outside, feeling happy
e) a passionate argument

i) a storm
ii) wind and driving rain
iii) snow
iv) blue skies and sunshine
v) cold, frosty and still

Q2 Finish this paragraph from a story, by describing weather to suit the character's mood:

"I'm going out!" shouted Abdi furiously, as he ran down the stairs.
Forgetting his jacket, he burst out of the front door and into the street.

Q3 People's names can show what their character's supposed to be like. Write down three of these names that you'd expect to be mean people if they were characters in a pantomime:

Mr Straightback
Mr Goodsoul
Mrs Pinchfist
Mrs Frostymouth
Ms Kindface
Mr Tightheart

I know, I know. This stuff is pretty blatant — you'd probably only use names like these in children's books or pantomimes.

Q4 Copy the descriptions below and write down a good name for each character. Try to make them a bit more subtle than I was in Q3.

a) a cruel nurse
b) a loving grandfather
c) a rich, mean old man
d) a tall, thin model

Quick way to create a descriptive surname: join an adjective with a part of the body. Easy.

It was a dark and stormy night...

...and the poor, overworked student sat in the top room of the tower, struggling to see the page in the flickering light, while thunder crashed and the wind roared... Feels like that sometimes, doesn't it.

Style and Organisation of Language

Q1 The following shopping list has been written in the form of a long paragraph that's difficult to read. Write it as a list, organising the items into groups.

> *Well, I think if I go into town I'm going to need some milk, because we always run out of milk. If we're going to have shepherd's pie tonight, I'm going to need some potatoes and some mince, and some onions. And some carrots as well. And if Anna brings her friend who likes cheese on the top, I'll have to get some cheese. For pudding, I don't know. Maybe a fruit salad. So I'll get some bananas, some oranges, maybe kiwi fruit if they've got them, and then cream! Mustn't forget cream! I think I'll get a couple of chicken breasts as well and keep them in the freezer. And Anna wants that new shampoo and we need some conditioner and cotton wool as well.*

Q2 *You lost your bag on the bus last week and you're writing to the bus company to see if they've found it.*

a) From the following, pick out the most important things to mention and write them down in a list:

- the contents of the bag
- what the bus driver was wearing
- how you felt when you realised
- your address
- the number of the bus
- there was a woman sitting next to you
- the time of the bus
- it was raining
- your contact phone number
- a description of the bag

b) Now write the letter to the bus company. It should be clear, concise and factual.

Q3 *A local politician wants more money for the children's ward in a nearby hospital. She has been asked to write an article about this for the local paper.*

a) Decide on a logical order for these parts of her article (write the letters down in the best order):

A: a paragraph including information about the increase in numbers of children in the local area over the last ten years
B: a graph showing the increase in the under-five population during the last ten years
C: a contact phone number
D: an appeal for interested people to contact the newspaper to help start a campaign
E: an instantly grabbing description of the sounds of children crying in an ambulance on the long journey to a faraway hospital
F: a paragraph including comments from the head of a sick children's support group
G: the headline
H: a photograph of a small baby

b) Write the article for the politician, using the structure you chose in part a), to persuade people to get interested in this issue.

Always in a logical order write you must...

Think of your audience. Never swear at children or old people and always be sarcastic to teenagers.

Choosing the Language and Style

Q1 Match each of these informal phrases with its formal equivalent from the box:

a) ain't
b) not likely!
c) gonna
d) hang on
e) I get it
f) ta

thank you
going to
that is not possible
please wait
am not *(or 'is not' etc)*
I understand

Q2 Look back at Q1. Write down three more examples of informal phrases, along with their formal equivalents.

Q3 a) Copy out this passage, underlining the words connected with sound:

Bang! She slammed the door shut, and stormed off down the corridor, her heels clicking on the hard floor.

Crash! The sound of crockery hitting the kitchen floor made him jump, as did the clattering of the cutlery following it.

b) Complete this passage with a paragraph that uses dramatic verbs and sounds to show the man's response:

Repetition of one word at the start or end of a story can be very effective. Look at this beginning:
Drip... drip... drip...
The prisoner looked into the blackness, and waited for the sound he most hated.

Q4 Here are four choices for the beginning of a story, each using repetition. Choose your favourite and continue the story.

A: Drip... drip... drip...
B: Hip, Hip, Hooray!... Hip, Hip, Hooray!... Hip, Hip, Hooray!
C: "Stop it! Stop it!"
D: Clink, clink.

Boring boring boring...

Only joking, English is great and wonderful and smashing and super. Isn't it? Hmmmmph... oh well — only 1 hour 10 minutes to go, then I'll be free, free, free...

Structuring Your Story

Q1 Write down the correct definition for each of these words (choose from the box):

a) flashback
b) retrospective
c) diary
d) narrator
e) narrative

- a book where you write your actions and thoughts
- when somebody suddenly remembers a past event
- the person telling the story
- the story
- looking backwards in time

Q2 Read this extract from a story, then write down the most likely reason that the man might have had a flashback:

He was sitting in the car, gazing out of the window at the crowds of faces, when suddenly, without warning, his mind was filled with the image of the house he'd tried hard to forget.

A: A smell triggered off the flashback.
B: He saw someone from the past.
C: He heard an old song.

Q3 Write a paragraph describing someone having a flashback because of a certain smell.

Q4 *Stories can be written in a different order from that in which the events happened.*

A series of events happened in this order:
Family win holiday to tropical island
Family arrive, get used to place
Family adopt a pet snake
Pet snake eats family members
Holiday representative discovers empty house

This is the order I'm going to write the story in:
Holiday representative discovers empty house (Flashback)
Family win holiday to tropical island
Family arrive, get used to place
Family adopt a pet snake
Pet snake eats family members

a) Write down one advantage of writing the story in the order the events happened.

b) Write down one advantage of writing the story starting with the ending.

c) Rearrange the following ideas to make a plan for a story that starts by creating suspense:

Man sees bright light.
Man goes into pub.
Man wakes up on Jupiter.
Man is walking home.
Aliens kidnap man.

Flashback! — "Ah, so THAT's what I did last night"...

Remember — stories don't have to be linear. Jumping backwards and forwards in time can add intrigue (or something) to your story. It's a handy trick — just so long as you don't overdo it. Or you'll just confuse your teacher, and that would never do.

Authors and Their Characters

A writer can use adjectives and adverbs to show how a character behaves.

Q1 a) Copy out these sentences, and underline the words that show how the writer changes our understanding of the character:

i) The victorious warrior queen rode triumphantly into the town.
ii) The cheating warrior queen rode shamefully into the town.

b) Write out two more sentences using this structure, filling in the blanks with your own choice of words:

The ______ warrior queen rode ______ into the town.

Q2 a) Copy out this extract from a play, using the best words from the choices in brackets.

Anna (shouting / happily)	*Where have you been? It's past midnight!*
Bobby (sulkily / lovingly)	*Nowhere.*
Anna (angrily / sweetly)	*What do you mean, nowhere?*
Bobby (loudly / enthusiastically)	*I was just out.*
Anna (offering him a chocolate / slamming down her book)	*Tell me the truth!*

b) Continue the scene for five or six lines, choosing adverbs or actions to show how the characters felt.

Q3 *It's useful to be able to see both the characters' feelings and the author's opinions or feelings. Read this extract from* The Lord of Castersugar *by Tommy Hardnut, then answer question 3.*

Mrs Trench's life became much more pleasant after she got married and moved into her husband's house. She busily redecorated, smartening the whole place up so she could be proud of it. Not a piece of paper was out of place, not a speck of dust was to be seen, and not a single spider was to be found spinning a web in a corner of the quaint Georgian windows. The garden didn't escape either. All the overgrown wild flowers, 'the weeds', which had made the garden their home, were torn up and replaced with tidy rows of pansies and primroses, and the lawn was trimmed to perfection. Even the iron railings outside the house, which had been happily rusting away at their own gentle pace for twenty years, got a new gleaming coat of paint to cover up their shame.

a) The passage talks about Mrs Trench redecorating the house. How does this make her feel? Pick the best answer from the choices below.

A: It makes her happy.
B: It makes her miserable.
C: It makes her nostalgic.

b) The redecoration is described in a positive way for Mrs Trench. But what else do you think the author might be trying to say? Pick the best answer from these choices:

A: The house looks really cool now.
B: The house was actually quite cool before all these changes.

Look mainly at the second half of the paragraph.

Author Daley — he was a great character...

It just goes to show — all authors are crafty little beggars. They play with your mind...

Personal Response

Q1 We've all read brilliant books and we've all read boring books. Think of the last fictional book you read and pick one or more reasons as to why you chose to read it in the first place.

a) the front cover
b) the blurb (the bit on the back)
c) the reviews
d) it was recommended by someone
e) you liked other books by the same author

Q2 What genre (type / style) was the story? *(e.g. horror, fantasy, adventure, romance etc.)*

Q3 There is usually a central or main character in a story. Name the character in the story and explain why they are central to the action.

Q4 Give definitions for the following types of main character:

a) protagonist

b) antagonist

Q5 Look at the following statements. Write down all the sentences that apply to the book you read. If none of them apply, write three similar sentences of your own that do.

a) The storyline seemed to drift without anything exciting happening.
b) This book was good but I wish the pace of writing had been quicker so I could get into the plot faster.
c) This book seemed to take a long time to reach a dramatic crisis point.
d) I felt like I really knew the characters as if they were real and when the crisis in the story came, I did really want to read on to find out what happened next.
e) I wanted to know what happened to the characters — I was disappointed when the plot finished without a satisfying resolution.
f) This book had such vivid descriptions I could actually imagine I was there!
g) I loved the twist at the end of the story.
h) I loved the cliffhanger end to this book — the writer let me decide for myself how the story ended.

Q6 Finish the following sentences to help you analyse why the book was brilliant or boring:

a) The [most intriguing / least exciting] character was … because...
b) The [most engaging / dullest] description in the book is where...
c) This book made me want to [keep turning the pages / stop reading and watch paint dry instead] because...
d) The ending of this book was [great / more disappointing than a wet lettuce] because...
e) I [would / wouldn't] recommend this book to … because...

Q7 As a matter of interest, what was the name of the book?

My personal response? — I reckon this book's great...

Book reviews. Never as much fun as reading the book, for sure. Still, you have to do them, so why not do them *well*. Rule no. 1: Summarising the plot is not enough. You need to do more than that to earn your brownie points. We're talking style of language, emotions, imagery, characters...

Interpreting Plays

Q1 These are all jobs to do with plays — match the descriptions to the jobs:

a) the person who writes the play
b) the person who tells the actors and the backstage staff what to do
c) the people (male or female) who take characters in plays
d) the person who whispers lines to actors who have forgotten what to say
e) the people who organise lights, sets, scenery, props etc.
f) the people who pay to watch the play

the audience
the actors
the prompt
the director
backstage hands
the playwright

Q2 Match up the following theatrical words to their definitions:

a) clothes worn by actors
b) painted background and furniture
c) the final practice of the performance
d) what the audience does to show they liked the performance
e) going on stage / going off stage
f) the first performance

i) entrances/exits
ii) scenery and sets
iii) costumes
iv) applaud
v) dress rehearsal
vi) opening night

A play is different from a novel because the audience can't just read about the thoughts in a character's mind. Instead, the actors have to show the audience how they are feeling.

Q3 Match the acting techniques in the box below to the appropriate example of how they could be used.

a) physicality (using movement)
b) facial expression (using the face)
c) body language (using the body)

i) raised eyebrows to show surprise
ii) folding arms to show a character is being defensive
iii) stamping off stage slowly and deliberately to show annoyance

Q4 Which of the following directions should the actors be aware of in order to communicate with the audience?

a) where to stand
b) where to move to
c) when to say their lines
d) if they should pause
e) all of the above

And whatever you do, don't mention the Scottish play...

...well don't. It's bad luck. Macbeth. Oooops. Ah well nevermind. Macbeth. Oh no I did it again.

Form and Meaning

Some poems have their own rules — like these rhyming couplets:

Ode to My Teacher Who Looks Like John Prescott
My teacher says I never use my brain
But then, I think she's probably insane
Chrissy Williams

Dear Sir
Sir is kind and sir is gentle
Sir is strong and sir is mental
Anon

Q1 Circle the rhyming words in the two couplets above.

Q2 Write a rhyming couplet where the word at the end of the first line is 'sky'. Now write two more rhyming couplets in the same way using the words 'tree' and 'fire'.

Rhyming couplets were used for ending ***sonnets*** *in Shakespearean times. Here's one taken from Shakespeare's Sonnet 18.*

So long as men can breathe, or eyes can see,
So long lives this, and this gives life to thee.

Often the first 12 lines of a sonnet explained a situation and then the last two lines summarised it.

Q3 How many lines are there in a Shakespearean sonnet?

a) three b) fourteen c) six

Stories written in verse and then ***sung*** *were very popular in the past, when not many people could read. This type of poem is called a* ***ballad****, and lots of poets have used this form.*

Q4 Which of the following examples is most likely to be a ballad? Say why.

a) Among twenty snowy mountains,
The only moving thing
Was the eye of the blackbird.

b) Of man's first disobedience, and the fruit
Of that forbidden tree, whose mortal taste
Brought death into the world, and all our woe..

c) There lived a wife at Usher's Well,
And a wealthy wife was she;
She had three stout and stalwart sons,
And sent them o'er the sea.

All over the world, different nationalities have used poetry to entertain people. In Japan, a really popular form of poetry is the Haiku, like the one in the box below.

Q5 Say how many syllables there are in the following lines:

a) the first line
b) the second line
c) the third line

Alone I cling to
The freezing mountain and see
White clouds below me
Ian Serriellier

Literary Heritage

The English language hasn't always been spoken and written how it is today — in fact it used to look pretty much like a foreign language and even had different letters!

Q1 On the left, below, are four stages of the English language. Match them up with the sentences on the right, which are examples of each of the four stages. (Each sentence means the same thing but looks different — don't worry if you don't understand the words.)

a)	Old English (AD 999)	i)	Now the elder son was out on the farm
b)	Middle English (AD 1380)	ii)	Forsoth his eldere sone was in the feeld
c)	Early Modern English (AD 1611)	iii)	Now his elder sonne was in the field
d)	Modern English (AD 1961)	iv)	Sōþlīce his yldra suna wæs on æcere

Books in Old English and Middle English times had to be written out by hand, mainly by monks, because there weren't any photocopiers back then.

Q2 Luckily, in 1476 a chap called Caxton stopped an awful lot of people from getting writer's cramp. Which of the following did Caxton invent?

a) the printing press b) wrist supports c) pencils

Q3 One seriously popular epic poem in Old English times was called 'Beowulf' all about a brave bloke who wanted to slay a dastardly dragon. It was written sometime between AD 700 and 900. Which of these is an extract?

a) The creature was like pestilence
Raging and ravenous, quick at his task,
Savage and unsparing ...

b) There is a lady sweet and kind,
Was never face so pleased my mind ...

Q4 *In Middle English times, Geoffrey Chaucer wrote 'The Canterbury Tales', all about a bunch of pilgrims entertaining each other with stories. Loads of people read Chaucer's stories — they liked them because he told the truth about people's personalities.*

At the time 'The Canterbury Tales' was written, French was a very important language in England. Why do you think Chaucer's tales were important for the English language?

a) They used a lot of puns and sarcasm.
b) They made English seem less important than French.
c) They encouraged people to read English and helped make the English language more important than French.

Q5 *The playwright and poetic idol of the Early Modern English period was good old William Shakespeare — he's a bit of a legend really. He added ten thousand neologisms (new words) to the English language. His plays dealt with universal themes and are still relevant to people's lives today. He invented great insults like 'you twangling lily-livered flibbertigibbet!'*

Make up your favourite Shakespearian insult using one word from each of the following boxes:

e.g. Why, you muggling, cream faced popinjay!

viperous, muggling, giddy, fuggling, twangling	hair brained, logger headed foul spoken, cream faced, stretch mouthed	ticklebrain, coxcomb, puke stocking, popinjay, flibbertigibbet

Planning and Presenting Ideas

Q1 These are all verbs. For each one, give a matching noun. *e.g. present → presentation*

a) plan
b) draft
c) edit
d) proofread
e) write

Think carefully about the meaning of these words in the context of writing an essay.

Q2 Your teacher thinks you're a fantastic student. You are asked to explain to another student why planning is a good idea before writing, and why proofreading is a good idea afterwards. Write a paragraph explaining this for your friend.

Q3 Match each term in the box with the correct description underneath.

brainstorming	journal	mental mapping

a) Somewhere where you write down your thoughts and feelings about events.
b) Using a mixture of diagrams, pictures and words to write your ideas on a page.
c) Working alone or with other people, writing down all the ideas you can think of.

Q4 Make up three **star charts** containing the following:

a) names of things (nouns) you might find in a jungle
b) verbs used to describe movement by humans or animals in a jungle
c) adjectives you would use to describe what it's like in a jungle

Q5 Use the words from Q4 to write a 10–line poem. Choose **one** of the titles below.

'Jungle Life'
'Strange Beauty'
'Night Creatures'
'From the Darkness'
'Survivor'
'Fever'

Q6 *You are the leader of a jungle safari trip. You are lost due to a tropical storm. Soon you will have to talk to the others and tell them your ideas. You only have half a sheet of A4.*

On your paper, use a **mindmap** structure to consider what you can do. Include pictures, symbols and key words. You do not have enough space for full sentences.

Q7 *Look at the diary entry below.* (Look up any words you don't understand.)

Midnight. −40°C. Have made a bivouac. Don't know how long I can go on. Still no sign of dogs. Can't feel toes. Hypothermia possible. Eating snow for water — lowering body temperature, but need water. Getting dehydrated from today's sun. God help me.

The writer was discovered semi-conscious by a rescue team the next morning. Using his diary entry, write the letter home to his family that he wrote the next day.

Handwriting

Q1 **Answer this quick quiz about handwriting.**

a) Are you left or right handed?
b) Do you print or use joined up writing?
c) For how many hours a day do you write?
d) Which do you write with more often — a pen or a keyboard?
e) Can other people read your writing?
f) Is your writing large, medium or small?
g) Do you write on the line?
h) Do you leave even spaces between the words?
i) Are your lower case letters all the same size?
j) Are your capitals all the same height?
k) Is your punctuation clear?
l) Is your writing the same as anyone's in your family?
m) Do you enjoy writing?
n) Do you have a favourite pen or pencil you enjoy using?
o) Do you like how your writing looks?
p) How has your writing changed in the last year?
q) How has your writing changed in the last five years?

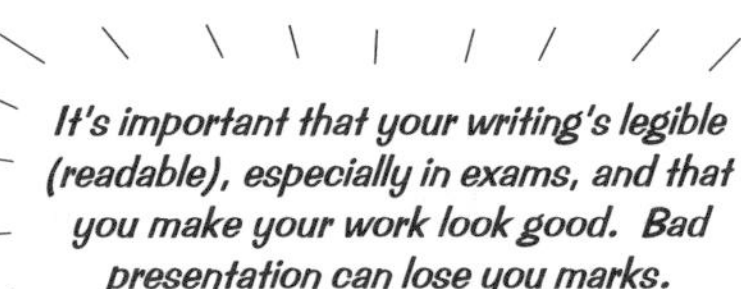

Q2 **Use your answers to the quiz to write a paragraph describing your handwriting at the moment.**

Q3 **Choose 5 words that describe how you would like your handwriting to look in the future. For each word, write 2 or 3 sentences to explain how this will happen.**

Q4 **The following passage (taken from 'An Inspector Calls' by J. B. Priestley) is very badly presented. Say how many ways you can spot to make it look better (there are at least 4).**

GERALD: You can drink to me.
SHEILA (*rising; QUIET AND serious now*) — **all right then.** *I drink to you, Gerald.*
GERALD (*quietly*): Thank you. And I drink to you — and hope that I can make you as happy as you deserve to be.
SHEILA You be c areful — or I'll start weeping.

Hint — think about fonts and spacing.

What do you mean — I need to work on my...

Of course it's boring to think about handwriting, but you and I both know it's important. To teachers. And examiners. Grrrrr...

Story Structure

Q1 Match up the following five parts of a story with their correct definition.

a) A **good opening**...
b) A **good developing plot**...
c) A **complication in a story**...
d) A **crisis** in a story...
e) A **satisfying resolution**...

i) ...should be an answer to or an explanation for the crisis in the story.
ii) ...should make the reader ask questions about the story.
iii) ...should make the reader see a problem and want to know if something worse will happen next.
iv) ...should give more detail to encourage the reader to begin to get answers to their questions and keep them reading.
v) ...should have the reader almost holding their breath and anticipating a solution.

Q2 Here's an example of a good opening — it's from R. L. Stein's 'The Barking Ghost'. Read it. Now write down three questions that you would like answered about the story.

I returned to the path again. But with my first step, I heard leaves rustling behind me.
I didn't turn round. I quickened my pace.
And I heard it again. Twigs snapping. Leaves rustling.

Q3 Here's the next bit — the **developing plot** — answer 'true' or 'false' for the following statements about how the writer has developed the plot.

My throat suddenly felt dry. Don't panic. Don't panic. 'Who — who's there?' I croaked.
No answer. I turned back.

a) It's extending the opening idea that 'something' is lurking behind.
b) It's letting us know that the person is getting more scared.
c) It's creating an atmosphere where we are still not sure if the something is real or not.
d) It's telling us exactly what the scary 'something' is.

Q4 Now for the **crisis**. What does the person in the story do that shows that this really is a crisis? Why does she do this?

Then I felt something horrible scrape my cheek.
Something cold. And sharp.
I couldn't help it. I started to scream.

Q5 *These notes show examples of the five typical parts of a story about Michael and David.*

The opening: Michael goes to David's house — the lights are off but there's an open door.
The developing plot: he walks in for a bit and looks around.
A complication: he can't believe his eyes — there is a trail of blood on the floor.
A crisis: he sees David dead in the bath.
A resolution: he finds the murderer and fights him to the death.

Write the story using the kind of detail that R. L. Stein might use. Stick to using those five parts of a story and expand on the detail with your own ideas.

Character

There are lots of ways to tell our reader about the personalities of the characters that we create in our stories.

Look at the description of Roy — you will get a pretty good impression of him quite quickly...

'Roy is one seriously grumpy man!' Steve said.
'Yeah he even growls at the checkout girl,' added Katie.
Roy was a grumpy man, no doubt about it.
He never smiled at his neighbours or said a friendly hello.
In fact, that very morning, grumpily, Roy thumped the television with his fist.
When his dog tried to wag at other dogs in the park, Roy always roughly dragged him away.

Q1 There is a word that describes Roy's personality — it appears, in slightly different forms, three times in three different sentences. What is the word?

Q2 Look at the sentences which contain the words you found for Q1. They tell us about Roy's personality in a really obvious manner. This is called being direct. Say which of these three sentences from the passage is described by each of the terms below.

a) direct action (tells you about the character by explaining what he does)
b) direct description (tells you about the character by describing his personality directly)
c) direct dialogue (tells you about the character by what someone directly says about him)

Q3 The remaining three sentences from the extract are not so obvious in the way they describe Roy. They are subtle (not obvious) and indirect, which means we have to think about the content to figure out his personality. Copy out those three sentences and say which of them is described by each of the terms below.

a) indirect description (the words in the story describe the character so that the reader makes up their own mind about the character's personality)
b) indirect dialogue (one person suggests something about a character through speech)
c) indirect action (the actions of a character are described but the reader is left to make up their own mind)

Q4 Using the last fiction book you read, make a chart and see if you can find an example of each kind of description from Q2 and Q3. (Make a note of the name of the book.)

My Uncle Roy — the meanest old idiot around...

Subtlety is the key, guys. Remember that. You'll get lots more presents that way.

Withholding Information

Writing stories is great fun (um...) but it's always good to know the tricks that keep your reader interested — like keeping the juiciest bits of your story till later...

Q1 Which word in the following sentence leaves the reader asking a question?

Something rustled in the darkness.

The answer to Q1 is known as an 'empty' word (meaning the reader doesn't know what the word applies to).

Q2 Write down one question the reader is left asking about the sentence in Q1.

Q3 What makes 'empty' words useful in storytelling? Choose one of the following answers.

a) they help to build up the suspense by making the reader read on to find out what the empty word means.
b) they help describe things in detail.
c) they tell you exactly what is going on

Holding back information is a really great way to keep your reader interested in your story — after all, a great story keeps you turning those pages wanting to know what happens next.

Another way to keep your reader interested in your story is to leave a chapter or a section of your story with an unanswered question or a crisis point where the reader is desperate to know the answer.

Aaron stopped suddenly — heart beating in his chest like a captured butterfly.
He stared into the darkness, ears straining for the tiniest whisper.
There it was again! That soft, snake-like hiss.
Out there, in that moonless, mist-shrouded night, something was moving...

Q4 What name is often given to this point in a story? Choose one of the answers below.

a) cliffhanger
b) compound sentence
c) an explanation

Q5 Write your own ending to a story which leaves the reader with an unanswered question. You can either choose one of the plotlines below, or make up your own.

a) waking up to the sound of heavy footsteps on the stairs
b) someone just about to find out their exam results
c) Beckham stepping up to take a penalty in the final of the World Cup (hey, we can dream)

YOU can't handle the truth — it's too pointy...

Most great scenes of suspense keep you guessing right till the last moment. Like now. Bet you can't guess what I'm going to say. That's right. Set elf to gurn. Bet you didn't see that coming...

Special Effects — Sounds and Images

Q1 **Match up the sentences with the same meaning and write them out in pairs.**

a) He was a tall man who looked very fierce.
b) She was a gentle person — she rarely told us off or criticised us.
c) She had a big hat with flowers, fruit and animals on top.
d) He was staring at the huge pile of ice cream.
e) The sun was shining on the tops of the trees.

You can make your writing more interesting by trying to create pictures in your reader's mind.

i) She was a gentle soul, never quick to scold or criticise.
ii) He was transfixed by the sight of the highest mountain of ice cream he had ever seen.
iii) He was a tall man with the demeanour of an ogre.
iv) The uppermost leaves were golden under the kiss of the evening sun.
v) Her hat was an elaborate edifice, from which a forest of flowers, fruit and intermittent wildlife spilled.

The sounds of language can also contribute to the effectiveness of your writing.

Q2 a) **Copy out the sentences, filling in each gap with one of the words from the box.**

i) She heard the pitter-patter of little feet .... across the wooden floor.
ii) The water .... slowly over the stones.
iii) There was a steady .... from the drum.
iv) The .... of leaves underfoot is a sure sign that autumn's here.
v) Her feet were .... and petite.
vi) He could hear the .... of teacups on the lawn.
vii) I've seen the sun on the .... sand.

neat silver chink rustle dripped bang-bang-bang scurrying

b) **For each sentence in part a), write out an appropriate description from this list.**

Short (quick) vowel sounds match the quick movement.
Long (slow) vowel sounds match the slow action.
The same sound occurs at the start of several words.
The added word sounds like the thing it describes.
The rhythmic sound matches the thing being described.
Word endings rhyme.

Q3 **You can use a repeated sound to build up an effect. Copy out these extracts, underlining the repeated sounds.**

a) The boiling broth bubbled on the bonfire.
b) Wet, weary, and worried, the wanderers returned.
c) She wore shiny shoes and a shimmering shawl.
d) the sound of the hissing and steaming stream
e) It was delicious and nutritious.

Q4 **Write five sentences or phrases of your own which use a repeated sound, as in question 3.**

Organising a Text

Q1 The second half of each question does not match the first half. Rewrite them so that each sentence is logical. I've done the first one for you.

a) There was a terrible noise coming from upstairs,
...so my granny hung her knickers out to dry.

a) There was a terrible noise coming from upstairs, so I banged on the ceiling with a broom.

b) There were only seconds left to act,
...so I put my feet up and relaxed.

c) I had completed my labours for the day,
...which caused me to panic and lose control.

d) It was blowing an absolute gale,
...so I banged on the ceiling with a broom.

Learn to ask yourself: "Does what I've just written make good sense to the reader?"

Q2 Write a sentence for each of these sets of words. Make sure that there is a clear link between the words as in the example below:

e.g. 'coward', 'fear', 'hero' — To become a true hero, the coward must first swallow their pride and face their darkest fear, alone.

a) 'jealousy', 'love'
b) 'cheat', 'winner'
c) 'ugly', 'beautiful'
d) 'crazy', 'genius'
e) 'disaster', 'triumph'
f) 'burp', 'explosion'
g) 'button', 'escape'
h) 'clear', 'silent', 'shot'
i) 'spy', 'Paris', 'film'
j) 'lion', 'train', 'sheep'
k) 'fight', 'run', 'camera'

Q3 Fill in the gaps in this text, using any combination of words you want. Just make sure that the story makes sense.

It .... as a foolish .... played on a friend but it turned into a .... for all concerned. We hung the .... out of the .... They .... just low enough so that the .... in the .... below could see them. My friend found it .... but her teacher thought the .... had fallen off the .... The teacher .... and looked like she was about to .... Everyone in our .... was .... and we all got .... for an hour after school.

What on earth are you on about?...

The words in a text can mean pretty much <u>anything</u> you want them to. Just make sure that you <u>signpost</u> your ideas for the reader and fully develop the links between causes and effects.

Presenting Information

Q1 You need to pick out the most relevant details when presenting information to the reader. Write down three relevant details about the following subjects and say why you think these points are the most important.

a) The classroom you are being taught in right now.

b) Your favourite television programme.

c) The Queen of England.

d) The village, town or city that you live in.

e) Your earliest memory.

Q2 It is a good idea to include factual examples when presenting information. Which of the following could be used in this way?

a) Many people listen to the radio.

b) The USA is the world's greatest superpower.

c) The USA is a very big country.

d) India is the largest democracy in the world.

e) There are 16 species of penguin living in the Southern Hemisphere.

f) Penguins can swim a long way under water.

Q3 Using a diagram to present your information can be a good way of attracting the reader's attention. Construct a diagram of your school building, and remember to label the important details.

Q4 Illustrations are an impressive way of capturing the reader's imagination. Draw a suitable illustration for this extract from the poem 'Jabberwocky'.

'Twas brillig, and the slithy toves
Did gyre and gimble in the wabe:
All mimsy were the borogroves,
And the mome raths outgrabe.

"Beware the Jabberwock, my son!
The jaws that bite, the claws that catch!
Beware the Jubjub bird, and shun
The frumious Bandersnatch!"

Extra, Extra, read all about it!...

When you're presenting information, do it in an imaginative and authoritative way. Grab the reader's attention and hold it by using appropriate details, examples, diagrams and illustrations.

Giving Instructions and Directions

Q1 Instructions should be very specific and easy to follow. Make a clear list of instructions for getting from start to finish of each of these tasks.

a) From buying a television set to watching 'Eastenders' on Sunday.

b) From having a toothache to sitting in the dentist's chair.

c) From being an apprentice Jedi Anakin Skywalker to becoming Darth Vader, Lord of the Sith.

d) From spilling some rice on the carpet to cleaning it up with a hoover.

e) From robbing The Bank Of England to lounging on a beach in Brazil.

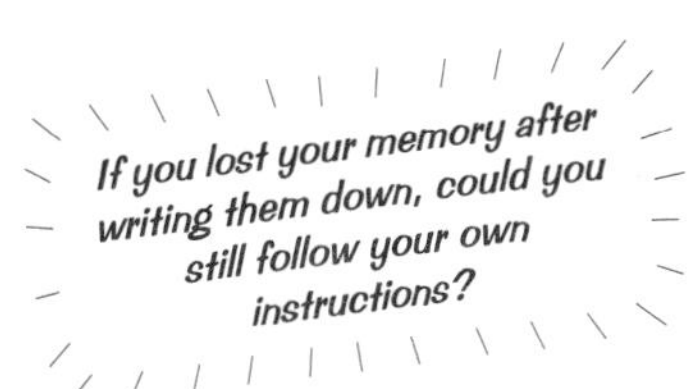

Q2 Write down a set of directions for getting from school to your house. Make them as clear as possible.

e.g. Leave the school gates. Turn right. Carry on straight ahead until you reach the traffic lights. Turn left...

Q3 Rewrite these sentences to complete the sequence of instructions properly.

a) Brush your teeth, walk to school, have some breakfast and get dressed.

b) Accelerate, put your seatbelt on, indicate to move out and start your engine.

c) Buy some souvenirs, put sun tan lotion on, fly to Morocco and have your immunisation shots.

d) Call an ambulance, cross the road, lie still on the ground and get run over.

e) Go to bed, have your evening meal, watch some television and get undressed.

f) Put the food in a bowl, give the bowl to the dog and open the tin of food.

g) Score a goal, do a little dance, kick the football and put on your boots.

Be methodical and economical when sharing your knowledge with the listener. You are answering a specific set of questions, not telling them how clever you are.

Wie komme ich am besten zum Bahnhof?...

Oops — wrong subject.

Making a Description

Q1 When making a description, you should begin by concentrating on the most relevant details. Circle the detail you think is the most important from each description, and explain the reason for your choice.

a) The pit bull was mottled, one-eyed, ferocious and muscular.

b) The firework was slow to start, bright red, deafening and short-lived.

c) The film was very long, about Samurai, set in Japan and subtitled.

d) The mountain was huge, windswept, beautiful and deadly.

e) The bus was packed, slow, stuffy and on time.

Q2 When you have found the most relevant details, the next step is to describe each detail accurately. Make an accurate description of the following objects.

a) your front door at home

b) an aircraft carrier

c) the World Cup trophy

d) a crystal ball

e) a CD

Q3 A description can also be used to set the mood of a scene. Try and describe these everyday settings in the most unusual ways that you can imagine.

a) a doctor's waiting room

b) a public, indoor swimming pool

Q4 Write a description of a person who is the exact opposite from the one described below.

> My driving instructor was an awful bore. He would sit next to me in perfect silence, keeping his eyes firmly on the road. If I drove too fast, he would stare hard at me and press gently on his instructor's brakes. If I ever got angry with other motorists, he would tell me to be more patient. When he drove home from the driving school, he observed all the rules of the road carefully, as he listened to Radio 2 on his little stereo. He would park his car perfectly on his drive, wipe his feet and peck his wife on the cheek. Yes sir, he was an awful bore.

Are you thinking what I'm thinking?...

Remember all your senses — sight, sound, smell, taste and touch. Write your descriptions from all possible perspectives and you might surprise the reader with your insight. You might.

Persuasive Writing

Q1 When expressing a personal view on a subject, you can emphasize your point by using exaggeration. Rewrite these sentences, exaggerating the situations as far as you can.

a) I fell onto my knees and scraped them quite badly.

b) She narrowly broke the school record for the 800 metres.

c) We had to speak louder to raise our voices above the music.

d) There was quite a mess in the room that morning.

e) I had an upset stomach yesterday.

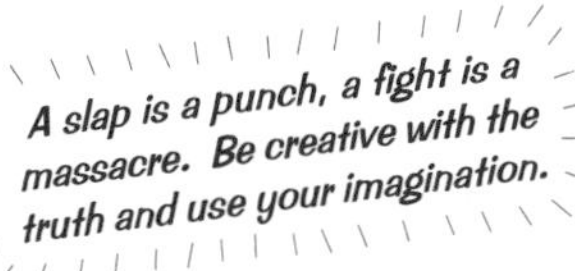

Q2 It can be useful to ask someone a 'rhetorical question' when the answer is obvious but you want to emphasize a point. Circle the phrases which can be used as 'rhetorical questions'.

a) Who are you?

b) Are you talking to me?

c) Is this a joke?

d) Where is it?

e) You don't mean that, do you?

f) Is she single?

g) What's all this then?

h) Are we there yet?

i) What colour is it?

j) What's that supposed to be?

k) Where are your manners?

l) Is it near here?

m) Who are you calling an idiot?

n) What time do you call this?

o) Are you deaf?

p) Are you OK?

Q3 Using repetition can also make your key points more persuasive, as it stresses the importance of what you have to say. Rewrite the sentences below so that they give the same opinion but in a different way.

a) I think cosmetic experimentation on dumb animals is cruel.

b) I believe that there is alien life on other worlds.

c) Replacing the British Pound with the Euro is a good idea.

d) I don't think Physical Education should be compulsory in schools.

e) Everyone is created equal.

I've told you a zillion times — don't exaggerate...

Get on your soapbox and get your opinion across to the masses. That's what this stuff's all about.

Holding an Argument

Q1 Providing statistical evidence is always a good way of supporting an argument. Suggest where you might find some figures to support the following arguments.

a) Fewer people bother to vote in each successive general election.

b) Glenn Rogers holds the world record for multiple badger juggling.

c) Cheeseburgers sell better than Big Macs.

d) Big Brother is the most popular programme on Channel 4.

Q2 The following are examples of bits of evidence used in court. Say which you think would be **good**, reliable bits of evidence and which would be **bad** bits of evidence.

a) A postman's personal opinions about what the suspect could have been thinking.

b) The testimony of someone who lived next door to the scene of the crime and who heard shouting on the night of the murder.

c) The criminal history of an armed robbery.

d) Fingerprints taken from the scene of the crime.

e) Showing what happened in an Oscar-winning film on the subject.

Q3 Quoting someone's testimony directly is a good way of making an argument more effective. Make up a quote from a 'star' witness in a trial, which would support each of these arguments.

a) He was with me at the time the murder took place.

b) She was at home on the night of the murder.

Q4 Underline all of the relevant points in this statement and make an argument from them. You should use all the techniques explored on this page to support your argument.

> I have never smoked a cigarette in my life but have contracted lung cancer at the age of 47. I was a pub landlord for twenty years before I became too ill to work but have been told that there is no definitive link between passive smoking and lung cancer. My wife has smoked for thirty years yet she seems perfectly healthy. She is terribly upset and feels guilty in some way. I just wish that I could find a way of proving the connection between the smoke that I breathed in for the last twenty years and the disease which is slowly killing me.

Arguing? I'm not arguing — you saying I'm arguing?...

Ahh... you can't beat a good argument. No, really, you can't. If someone's got a really good argument, with loads of evidence and examples, it's really hard to argue against it. Don't you find..?

Offering Informal Advice

Q1 When writing informal advice, you must think about who's going to be reading it. Look at these descriptions and write down some issues that you would advise each person to think about.

a) I'm an English teacher being offered one year's work in Japan.
e.g. Think about whether you want to move to Japan, whether you want to be a teacher, and how easy or difficult it will be to learn Japanese.

b) I'm an athelete whose leg has been seriously broken.

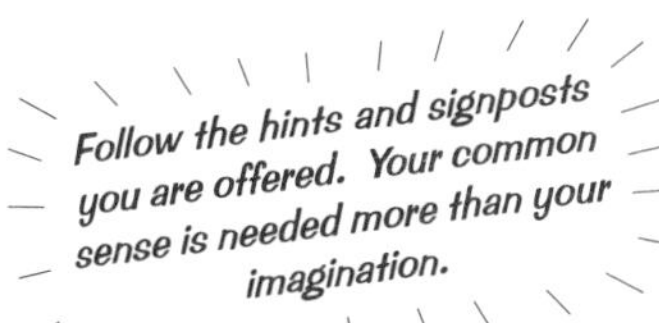

c) I'm a pop star whose band is splitting up.

d) I'm a preacher who has lost his faith.

e) I'm at a boarding school and am tired of being bullied.

f) I'm a coal miner who has lost his job.

Q2 Spot which of the following is offering advice unsuccessfully, and say why you think it's bad.

a) You should always check your change when out shopping.

b) It's a good idea to brush your teeth before going to bed.

c) You should treat others as you wish to be treated yourself.

d) If you don't cross the road sensibly you're a total idiot.

Q3 Using your English teacher as the intended reader, consider the following viewpoints and decide whether he or she would answer 'True' or 'False' to them.

a) Aggressive beggars should be banned from town centres.

b) Too much television rots the mind.

c) The number of pupils in each lesson should be smaller.

d) Hollywood films are all a load of rubbish.

e) I enjoy teaching English.

The Doctor said it was too late, Jill's mind had rotted

I know it's none of my business, but...

There's nothing less welcome than unwanted advice. But the least you can do is make the advice constructive — by anticipating your readers' needs, interests and views. Put yourself in their shoes.

Evaluating the Situation

Q1 I recently went on a trip to the zoo. Here are some things that happened. Sort them into two lists, one for good points and one for bad.

The lions escaped and ate my uncle.

The elephants still have my wallet.

A monkey smiled at me.

I was allowed to feed the seals.

The boa constrictor ate one of the meerkats.

I was allowed to stroke lots of cute piglets.

I dropped my camera into the penguin pool.

I ate ice cream.

An 'evaluation' involves taking stock of a situation and presenting your findings. It means trying to sum up all the good and bad points about something.

Q2 Write down a list of things you should think about when evaluating the following:

e.g. a car accident — what damage was done, whose fault it was, how much repairs will cost etc...

a) a burglary

b) an English lesson

c) a job interview

d) a rehearsal

Q3 Give some ways in which you might evaluate the success or failure of the following events:

e.g. How many people attended...

a) The Olympic Games.

b) The Queen's Golden Jubilee.

Q4 Write down two different evalautions from the following description. Make one as fairly balanced as possible, and write the other as if you were Jeff's mum.

The next contestant in the local talent contest was Jeff Green, singing a compilation of Elvis Presley's greatest hits. He swung his hips from side to side like a lunatic, screaming the lyrics into his microphone like there was no tomorrow. At one point, he fell backwards off the stage over a loose cable but continued to sing without a pause. There was a gasp from the audience. Then his sequined pants fell down around his ankles and his purple teddy bear underpants were exposed to screams of laughter. When he finished, there was a huge cheer from everyone but whether this was out of approval or out of sympathy, who could say?

How to make friends and influence a goat...

Your evaluation may actually change someone's opinion, so you need to ask yourself both "what do I think?" and "do I want to influence the way other people think?"

Reflecting Upon a Text

Reflecting upon a text means writing down, or telling someone, what we think about it.

Q1 Consider and write down your responses to the following statements:

a) I don't care about starving people in other countries.

b) School is a complete waste of time.

c) Money can buy you anything.

d) Music can make us either happy or sad.

e) There is no time like the present.

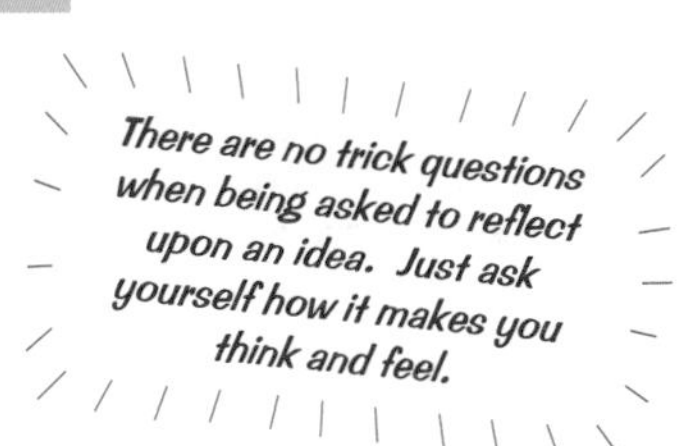

Q2 Write a reflective sentence on any subject you want, using each of the words below. Your answers should reflect your own personal opinions.

Example: "furious" — When I see wild animals performing in a circus, I feel furious.

a) worried
b) confused
c) happy
d) impatient
e) sad
f) frustrated
g) excited
h) uncertain
i) interested
j) motivated
k) reassured
l) entertained
m) angry
n) terrified
o) relaxed
p disgusted
q) enthralled
r) loved

Q3 You should be sympathetic to the needs of others who might read your reflections upon a text. Do these reflections take other people's views into consideration? Answer 'yes' or 'no'.

a) "Anyone who believes in fairies is an idiot."

b) "That film was just not to my taste."

c) "There is no excuse for that sort of behaviour."

d) "I find it hard to understand why anyone would take part in a war."

e) "I stand by what I've just said."

Mirror mirror on the wall...

Think of reflections in a mirror — they can easily get distorted. If you express your opinions at the expense of someone else's feelings, your point may get twisted in the process.

The Answers

Section One
Spelling

Page 1

Q1 Th(e) f(a)t m(a)n broke th(e) chain (o)n h(i)s bike (o)n the way t(o) th(e) qu(i)z show.

Q2 a) rain, snail, main, sail, fail
stay, spray, play, clay, today
brake, snake, make, place, same
b) ai, ay, a-e

Q3 a) playground
b) snakes
c) brake
d) rains, day
e) same
f) make, clay
g) snail, train
h) explain, again

Q4 a) beat, team
b) light
c) height
d) eat, meat
e) cheat
f) bite

Page 2

Q1
int(e)rested	veg(e)table	fatt(e)ning
tot(a)lly	necess(a)ry	def(i)nit(e)ly
eas(i)ly	Wedn(e)sday	diff(e)rence

Q2 a) boundary
b) deafening
c) desperately
d) library
e) primary
f) frightening
g) separated
h) voluntary

Q3 a) fitted, trapped
b) hopping
c) hoped, rabbits
d) hooting
e) stopped
f) sawed, sitting
g) staring
h) starring.

Q4 a) The (c)elebrity cuddled his cat in the (c)entre of the (c)emetery.
b) circle, century, ceiling, city, cellar, cement, circus, cinder.
c) e, i

Page 3

Q1 a) benches
b) sweets
c) dogs
d) witnesses
e) files
f) buses
g) waltzes
h) foxes

Q2 **-ies**: baby, ruby, story, sky, fly
-s: monkey, subway, key, spray, valley
any reasonable sentences accepted

Q3 My favourite animal is a donkey. One of the reasons I like donkeys is that they have great long ears. Their favourite hobbies are eating, sleeping and playing frisbee. The older ones don't play frisbee though — instead they go to buy meat and vegetables, and make gravy. I used to have lots of fields to keep donkeys in, but ever since it rained cats and dogs last Tuesday, I have to keep them all in boxes. I don't think they like it much in there, but I've promised to give them all pet puppies if they promise not to behave.

Page 4

Q1 a) radios, videos, stereos (in any order)
b) echoes
c) kilos
d) heroes
e) potatoes, tomatoes (in any order),
f) stilettos.

Q2 The chiefs' wives had started putting their loaves up on high shelves and covering them with handkerchieves/ handkerchiefs because the wolves kept behaving like thieves and stealing them. This frightened the calves in the hills and they kept running towards the cliffs in panic. This was threatening the lives of all the chiefs' people. It also left marks of hooves/hoofs in the loaves, so something had to be done.
"We'll have to get the dwarves/dwarfs in," said the chief.
The dwarves/dwarfs sharpened their knives, wrapped themselves in thick scarves/scarfs and hid in the leaves to wait for the wolves. The wolves, who were not stupid, pushed the calves on top of the dwarves/dwarfs and stole the loaves in the panic. The dwarves/dwarfs flounced off, saying,
"That's it. You'll have to sort it out yourselves."

Page 5

Q1 a) curable, videoing, excited, noticing, responsible, shaking, lovable, taxied
b) describing/describable/described, moving/movable/moved, skiing/ skiable/skied, aging/aged (ageing also acceptable as exception to rule), sensing/sensible/sensed, managing/manageable/managed, adoring/adorable/adored, debating/ debatable/debated, echoing/ echoed

Q2 a) She was careful not to disturb anyone as she crept in.
b) At ten to four, everyone had gone home and the school was peaceful.
c) He desperately wanted to be allowed to go on the trip.
d) Finishing the race in such a short time was a tremendous achievement.
e) Don't throw that away, it could be useful.
f) He was a good advertisement for his school.
g) You must measure ingredients accurately or the recipe won't work.

Page 6

Q1 The misspelt words should be —
a) enjoying
b) hungrier
c) business
d) playing
e) laid
f) prettiest
g) reliable
h) unemployable
i) dried

Q2 a) motion
b) nation, politician
c) collision
d) occasion
e) optician
f) attention
g) population

Page 7

Q1 a) unhappy
b) unclean
c) inactive
d) unbroken
e) invisible
f) uncover
g) undress
h) unfair

The Answers

Q2 a) irresistible, illegible, impossible, impatient, immature, illegal
b) i) impossible
ii) illegal
iii) irresistible
iv) immature
v) impatient
vi) illegible

Page 8

Q1 a) E
b) B
c) A
d) F
e) D
f) G
g) C

Q2 a) advice
b) quiet
c) allowed
d) bought
e) are
f) too, to
g) threw, through
h) practice
i) breaking
j) effect

Page 9

Q1 a) that's
b) don't
c) you're
d) they'll
e) can't
f) who's

Q2 a) can't
b) he'll
c) that's
d) we're
e) they're
f) won't
g) shan't

Q3 a) the rabbit's hutch
b) Nat's football
c) Carlos' scar
d) the truck's wheel
e) the horse's leg
f) the video's label
g) the cliff's edge

Page 10

Q1 The plural forms should be —
a) boys'
b) ladies'
c) babies'
d) footballers'
e) nurses'
f) hours'

Q2 a) men's
b) aircraft's
c) children's
d) sheep's
e) lice's

Q3 a) I've got my lunch, but I didn't pick yours up.
b) Jon said the book was his but Sunita said it was hers.
c) I'm sure it's hurt, it's got its wing stretched out.
d) Tom's drawing is bigger, but I think mine's better.
e) When we've finished rehearsing, they'll perform theirs first and then we'll do ours.

Page 11

Q1 a) spelling exercise (no answers)
b) dictionary exercise

Page 12

Q1 a) fierce
b) alcohol
c) texture
d) knowledge
e) strength
f) caught
g) shoulder
h) fulfil
i) happened
j) although
k) people
l) surprise

Q2 a) She wrote in her journal every day for thirty years.
b) Lee decided it would cause too much embarrassment to announce his feelings in front of everyone.
c) The younger you are, the more interest you have in looking after the environment.
d) The sides of a square or rectangle are parallel.
e) Everyone on the trip must remember a packed lunch.
f) No one ever listens to what their mother tells them.

Q3 One syllable:
wrist
sand
noon
scrunch
sell
scout
knife
send
Two syllables:
bias
diet
engage
repeat
island
trotting
risen
toga
challenge
grating
Three syllables:
beautiful

Page 13

Q1a) i) The bright light in the middle of the night gave the knight a right fright.
ii) Dancing was a habitual part of the actual ritual.
iii) His daughter was taught that laughter was the wrong response to slaughter.
iv) He coughed as he ploughed through the tough troughs and rough boughs.
v) The astounding sound of the bounding hound surrounded the mound that they stood around.
vi) The repair of the chair brought despair to the hairy fairy.
b) any reasonable answers

Q2 a) to h): any reasonable answers (that are found in the dictionary)

Q3 a) an undertaker
b) love of mankind
c) an opinion, fitting in with what has always been believed

Page 14

Q1a) i) deceive
ii) donkeys
iii) torches
iv) sheep
v) swimming

The Answers

b) i) **i** before **e** except after **c**
ii) words ending in **y** — if there's a vowel before the **y**, you just add **-s** to make it a plural
iii) if a word ends in **-ch** you add **-es** to make it a plural
iv) the plural of sheep is the same as the singular
v) double consonant before **-ing** when there's a short-sounding vowel

Q2 a) accept
b) quite
c) write
d) knew
e) their

Q3 any reasonable answer

Q4 a) wrong — I've been practising my juggling skills for months.
b) right
c) wrong — Jimbo ran past the lion-tamer with a smile.
d) right
e) right
f) wrong — There's a bomblike device strapped to the hymn book.
g) wrong — I passed my exams really easily.
h) wrong — There just aren't enough good hairdressers in the world.
i) right
j) wrong — Where are the best places to eat toffee around here?

Page 15

Q1 a) psychology, monarchy, psychiatrist
b) immediately, fortunately
c) dependent, permanent, convenient
d) psychology, psychiatry
e) necessary, misspelt, immediately, accommodation, irregular
f) responsible (definite)
g) successful, beautiful
h) receive
i) separate (necessary, irregular)
j) persuade
k) people

Q2 any reasonable answers

Section Two Vocabulary

Page 16

Q1 a) i) devoured
ii) nibbled
iii) gnawed
iv) masticated
v) munched

b) [dictionary exercise]
students' answers should use words in an appropriate context

Q2 a) mammoth, enormous, huge, large
b) microscopic, miniscule, tiny, little
c) ecstatic, delighted, pleased, satisfied

Q3 [dictionary exercise]
students' answers should use words in an appropriate context

Q4 students' answers should use reasonable replacements for 'nice' and 'good' in the given paragraph.

Page 17

Q1 [thesaurus exercise]

Q2 [dictionary exercise]

Q3 a) Aboriginal
b) French
c) Italian
d) Persian
e) Hindustani
f) Arabic
g) Dutch
h) Nahuatl
i) Greek
j) Sioux

Page 18

Q1 [dictionary exercise]

Q2 [dictionary exercise]

Q3 [dictionary exercise]

Page 19

Q1 noun — is a person, place or thing
verb — is a doing or being word
auxiliary verb — helps the main verb in the sentence
adjective — describes a noun
adverb — describes a verb
preposition — introduces a phrase about time or place
conjunction — joins two sentences or parts of a sentence
article — introduces a noun

Q2 a) Francesca — noun
b) bicycle — noun
c) in, under — both prepositions
d) and, but — both conjunctions
e) the, an, a — all articles
f) hard, accurately — both adverbs
g) skated, crashed — both verbs
h) had, was — both auxiliary verbs
i) exhausted, elated — both adjectives

Q3 students' answers should show correctly underlined words

Page 20

Q1 a) mostly
b) partially
c) hardly
d) slightly
e) usually

Q2 students' answers should show correct use of qualifiers

Q3 students' answers should show correct use of singular/plural nouns in these sentences.

Q4 students' answers should show correct use of comparative terms

Page 21

Q1 a) falsify
b) testify
c) glorify
d) specify
e) magnify

Q2 a) interference
b) existence
c) dedication
d) graduation
e) persistence
f) insistence
g) participation
h) complication
i) elevation
j) reference

Q3 a) fantasize — fantasy
b) hypothesize — hypothesis
c) criticize — crticism
d) publicize — publication

Q4 a) untidy
b) depart
c) dissatisfaction
d) reapply
e) unwind
f) disapprove
g) unbalanced
h) unsatisfactory
i) disconnect
j) decode
k) unhinged

Page 22

Q1 a) during
b) whilst
c) meanwhile
d) before
e) for the whole time

The Answers

Q2 students' answers should show correct use of linking words

Q3 accept any reasonable answers

Q4 students' answers should show correct use of linking words for time, reason and speculation

Page 23

Q1 any reasonable answers

Q2 any reasonable answers — for example:
- b) 'formula' might be used in Maths to calculate a quantity
- c) 'vocabulary' might be used in French for lists of translated words
- d) 'observations' might be used in Chemistry for noting changes in a chemical reaction
- e) 'cell' might be used in Biology, e.g. when comparing plant and animal cells

Q3 any reasonable answers

Section Three Sentences and Paragraphs

Page 24

Q1
- a) My brother is happy when his team wins.
- b) As the plane takes off I watch the wings vibrate.
- c) He stopped reading because the monster was making him scared.
- d) Whenever he chased his tail, the dog ran in circles.
- e) Although she felt sad, she sang at the concert.

Q2
- a) Keen to go home, Roy threw a tantrum.
- b) Speaking from his heart, he displayed how he really felt.
- c) My barber, who was very wealthy, cut his prices.
- d) Whenever it snows, the mountains look beautiful.
- e) The DVD, which I bought yesterday, was already damaged.
- f) Until the bridge was built, people crossed the river by boat.

Q3 any reasonable answers: the following are examples:
- a) After running the marathon, Sarah was exhausted.
- b) Tom, whenever he answered a question, felt 6 feet high.
- c) Since she had been 12, Jade had dreamt of being on TV.
- d) Kate cleaned her teeth every night before getting into bed.
- e) Austin danced like a madman, until he dropped.
- f) Julie searched for the papers like a bull in a china shop.
- g) For no reason at all, Jennifer screamed at the top of her voice.
- h) If only for effect, Jill laughed heartily.
- i) Because of the terrible smell, Viv covered her face.
- j) However he twisted and turned, he could not shake off his attackers.
- k) Jake still felt pretty happy, despite the fact that his dog had just died.

Q4
- a) I've just bought Rap 212's new album which is awful.
- b) It's for my best friend John who lives in New York.
- c) It was in Devon where there was a terrible outbreak of Foot and Mouth disease.
- d) I meant the bottle of lemonade which has probably gone flat.
- e) Sarah, who is packing for her holidays, is a bit tired.

Page 25

Q1 any reasonable answers — the following are examples:
- a) John, travelling by train, was going to visit his grandma.
- b) Sabrina, wearing her favourite dress, chose to walk to the party.
- c) Growling at the man the dog moved closer to him.
- d) Hoping her pet was still inside, she opened the door of the cage.
- e) The manager, in a desperate hole, mumbled that it was a game of two halves.

Q2 any reasonable answers, for example:
- a) Going to her grandmother's, Red was eaten by a wolf.
- b) Having eaten all that pie, Becky felt quite sick.
- c) Staying as far from the edge as possible, Simon edged towards the summit.
- d) Wearing nothing but his pants, Phil ran embarrassed through the park.
- e) Wanting to know just what had happened, Uda peered through the window.

Q3 any five further reasonable answers as in Q2

Q4
- b) She had a devilish grin, like all fiends.
- c) He burned to play again, despite losing all his matches.
- d) Until the onions turn a golden brown, do not add the celery.
- e) Everyone must evacuate the building when the bell rings.

Q5 any suitable clauses, for example:
- a) The knife, which was used in the murder, was sharp.
- b) Henry, who was always greedy, wanted an eighth course.
- c) In America, where they have different sports than we have here in Britain, they play baseball.
- d) The detective, who doubted what he'd heard, drove to the scene of the crime.
- e) Diana, who was humouring the boring man, laughed at the joke.
- f) On Friday, which is the day after tomorrow, we will feed the penguins.
- g) Dangerous creatures, which had never been seen before, roamed the jungle.

Page 26

Q1 any suitable adjectives, for example:
- a) The hysterical girl shouted.
- b) A speeding car crashed.
- c) The silly boy cried.
- d) The tiny baby slept.
- e) The enormous alligator snapped.

Q2 any suitable prepositional phrase, for example:
- a) The girl shouted in the street.
- b) A car crashed into the church wall.
- c) The boy cried in his bedroom.
- d) The baby slept in its cot.
- e) The alligator snapped at the zoo keeper.

Q3
- a) Bad Alice screamed at her brother.
- b) The boy slumped over his literacy booklet.
- c) The American soldiers landed at four o'clock.
- d) He hurled the stone through the window.
- e) His computer exploded with a bang.

Q4
- a) The rabid dog leapt at the crowd outside the kennels.
- b) Stanley arrived with his mum.
- c) She hid behind the shed.
- d) The sports car was delivered to the garage before lunch.
- e) Tired and upset, the policeman bellowed at the burglar in the garden.
- f) Leonardo, impatient to draw, scratched into the rock.

The Answers

Page 27

Q1 These are examples — some answers may be punctuated slightly differently.
- a) Don't forget that tomorrow is sports day. The whole school will be ending lessons after period three.
- b) Tomorrow we're starting our project on newspapers. Don't forget to bring in a newspaper if you have one.
- c) We've run out of tea. Can you get some from the shop on your way home?
- d) The music was great, though I'm not sure about the dancing. I don't think I could do all those high kicks.
- e) Sheep are strange animals. They're quite sweet, though; the lambs are particularly cute, especially when they're very young.
- f) When I was little we lived in the North. People called you "luv" when they spoke to you. Then we moved further south.
- g) He's fond of that desk because it was his grandfather's. I bet it can tell some stories. His grandfather used to do all his letter-writing at that desk; he was always writing to politicians and to the newspapers.

Q2
- a) Let me know if you want to come.
- b) Would the person who left their keys in the foyer please collect them from reception?
- c) I'll put you in touch with my elder sister, who has a lot of experience in this area.
- d) There are several new tracks, many of which are completely different from the old stuff.
- e) I met a lot of interesting people, some of whom I really liked.
- f) She told him that she loved him.
- g) My computer's not working, which is a real pain.
- h) She mentioned several things that were bothering her.

Q3
- a) Next week we will be making meringues. You will need the following ingredients: sugar and egg whites.
- b) Oven temperature is very important in making meringues; it needs to be very low. If you are using an electric oven, you can turn it off after a certain amount of time and leave the meringues in the oven while it cools down.
- c) When your meringues are completely cool, you can sandwich them together with fresh cream. Alternatively, you can drizzle melted chocolate over them.
- d) Can you think of alternative fillings for your meringues? Write your suggestions down in your notebook. (You can write down something you have eaten before, or something that you would like to try.)

Page 28

Q1
- a) He had been voted out by viewers who were fed up with his behaviour. / He has been voted out by viewers who are fed up with his behaviour.
- b) We had rung them to ask if they were coming the next day.
- c) She can't promise to solve all of their problems, but she will try. / She couldn't promise to solve all of their problems, but she would try.
- d) My printer had broken and so I needed to go shopping. / My printer has broken and so I need to go shopping.
- e) What if no one comes / came?
- f) The government was keen to explore various options and had decided to act as soon as possible. / The government is keen to explore various options and has decided to act as soon as possible.

Q2
- b) I phoned the garage earlier about the car (1). They said they could only do it next week (2). They also said it would cost two hundred pounds (3). So I'm going to ring round some other garages (4).
- c) The party was a big success (3). So much so, in fact, that it's been suggested it should be an annual event (4). What no one realises is that the building almost caught fire an hour before everyone arrived (1). Luckily we put it out and the rest went smoothly (2).
- d) Last night mum said I should have an evening without watching TV (2). I didn't agree, as I really wanted to see the concluding part of a particular programme (3). I'd watched the first half of it last week (1).

Q3
- b) A new system has been introduced.
- c) Several important points have been forgotten.
- d) The school has been visited by several famous people over the years.
- e) The whole house had been cleaned from top to toe.
- f) She was admired by all of us.
- g) Their hair had been washed and their faces scrubbed.
- h) All of the applicants had been interviewed.

Page 29

Q1
- b) Not clear if the forms are the parents' or the young children's.
  Better if it said:
  If you have young children, please return their forms as soon as possible.
- c) Not clear if the students are asking if they can help or asking the teachers to help them.
  Better if it said:
  The students asked the staff if they would be prepared to help.
- d) Not clear if the toys or the pictures are free.
  Better if it said:
  If you find any free pictures of toys, please bring them along.

Q2
- a)
  - i) In the first sentence, "however" means "in whatever way".
  - ii) In the second sentence, "however" means "but" or "even so".
- b) The hyphen shows you that "designer-name" is describing something that follows (otherwise it could be a "name-bag" that is "designer").
- c) The comma after "this" is telling you where to pause. If you don't pause here, the beginning of the sentence sounds like the other sentence.
- d) The commas in the first sentence show you that you're including some extra information — you can understand the sentence without it. In the second sentence, there's no comma after "book", so the next bit is saying which book you mean.

Q3
- a) Sports Day is fun, although it can be rather embarrassing. When you're little your mum comes and cheers you on, makes you wear your sunhat (even though it's normally raining), and joins in the parents' races. Sometimes there's a teachers' race, too. By the time you get to senior school <u>the mums</u> usually stay at home, although you still have to participate whether you're sporty or not. The sixth formers are supposed to look after the younger ones, although <u>neither group is usually</u> happy about this. <u>Basically,</u> I think Sports Day should be optional and the rest of us should have the time off. After al<u>l,</u> the effort of organising it isn't necessarily matched by the amount of enjoyment it generates.

The Answers

b) i) they = the mums (not the teachers)
ii) "they" could be the sixth formers, the younger students, or both
iii) "At the end of the day" sounds as if you're going to talk about what happens at the end of Sports Day.
iv) The comma after "after all " makes it easier to predict the rest of the sentence.

Page 30

Q1 a) "Have you got the sheepdog back yet?" asked Jeremy.
b) Cathy looked a bit taken aback, but replied, "No. The church was fine last time I looked."
c) "Jess is lying down now." Mary sounded relieved and sat down.
d) I didn't know what to say; "Oh," I muttered.
e) "When is a raven like a writing desk?" he asked us slowly, "and how do you know?"
f) "Naz, if you don't give Adam's shoes back right now," he yelled, "I swear you'll regret it."
g) "Where," he asked, in a moment of silence, "would you start looking for my handbag?"

Q2 (Answers may vary slightly, but anything reasonable is fine.)
b) "I think white stilettos are dead classy," said Shania proudly.
c) "Elvis is not dead. He's just resting," said Shania seriously.
d) "My uncle used to be a rabbit," said Shania apologetically.
e) "Don't ever borrow my fishnets again," shouted Shania angrily.

Q3 a) "I have been meaning to talk to you about that," he said with a smile."
b) Nasser wasn't sure how to respond. "Maybe later," was just about all he could say.
c) "Haven't the penguins been sleeping in the tool shed?" asked Marion in horror.
d) "I have a dream," she said, "and it involves a big plate of waffles."
e) "It wasn't me," she said, carefully slipping the goldfish back into the bowl.
f) "How exactly," he said looking mean, "do you think we're going to get to Fiji?"
g) "It's not a question of who feeds him," Henry started. "It's a question of how much he gets fed." So that was that. "Unless we just go with the peanuts again," he added.

Page 31

Q1 a) matches B
b) matches C
c) matches A
d) matches D

Q2 any reasonable answer

Q3 any reasonable answer

Page 32

Q1 a) Scientists have suggested more than eighty reasons why dinosaurs died out on our planet.
b) It's not surprising that the few escape attempts from Alcatraz ended in failure.
c) The car being written about is a very good one, if you believe the manufacturer's hype.

Q2 c)

Q3 a) "It is never too late to give up cigarettes for the sake of your health."
b) "They were first called this because the pilot literally hangs underneath the glider's large triangular wing."
c) "The 20th June was the most difficult day that I had faced since I had started at the school."
d) "I like to write stories but I find spelling really difficult even with a dictionary."

One of these will then be developed into a full paragraph. Any reasonable answer may be accepted.

Page 33

Q1 a) A man nearly fell to his death yesterday when daring thieves made off with his set of ladders. 38 year old Gary Chamois, a professional window-cleaner, had his ladders stolen from him while he was cleaning an upstairs window. Gary, a father of two, had stepped onto a ledge to reach the windows and it was at this time that the ladders were stolen. He first realised the ladders were gone when he stepped back and slipped, sending his bucket and wash leathers plummeting 15 metres to the ground. Gary, who had to be rescued by the local fire brigade, was said to be feeling a bit down about the whole thing.
b) Melinda Metaphor's new single sold more copies on the first day of release than any other single in history. Some dedicated fans camped all night outside of record stores in order to be the first to buy. Melinda is aged 20 and her mum is a hairdresser. Melinda is now working on her next album for release later in the year.

Q2 Any reasonable answer — for example: The Ford Zippy has power steering, *whereas* the Chrysler Fantasy has computer-controlled ignition. The Zippy uses a new low-pollution fuel, *while* the Fantasy is powered by batteries. *Although* the Zippy has been designed to be very economical, the Fantasy is extremely comfortable.

Q3 I opened my eyes. It was still pitch black outside. Then I heard the howl. It sent spine-tingling shivers flashing down my back. I pulled the blankets over my head but I could still hear the howling. I broke into a sweat and my teeth chattered with fear. Still the howling continued. Eventually, reluctantly I decided I had no choice — I had to get up and let the dog in.

Page 34

Q1 a) Singing at the top of my voice, I enjoyed my first hot bath in a week.
b) Leaping out of the burning plane, the stuntwoman pulled her ripcord at the very last moment.
c) Before being rushed to hospital, the scout leader had assured all the scouts that a sharp knife was a safe knife.

Q2 any reasonable answer — for example: The bus chugged out of the bus station, changing gear as it climbed the hill out of the town, then at the top it built up speed, its engine roaring until it went even faster while the passengers were thrown from side to side, then, still accelerating down the hill, the driver shouted out that the brakes had failed, and jumped out of his cab at the last moment.

Q3 any reasonable answer — for example: The tired climber grabbed hold of the rope. He pulled hard on it to make sure it was secure. Then he began to climb. He breathed hard. The air was thin at this height. His oxygen had run out. Slowly he lifted one foot after the other. His hands grappled for handholds. He moved incredibly slowly up the sheer rock face. His left foot slipped on a chunk of ice. He grabbed out with his right hand. He found to his horror that his rope was snapping. He reached for a hold on the rock. It was too late. He fell off and out into thin air. He was never seen again.

The Answers

Q4 any reasonable answer — for example: But how it had gone wrong! What a mess! What a mistake! Another mistake! Never again!

Page 35

Q1 the best order for the paragraphs is: E; D; B; A; C

Q2 any reasonable answers — for example:
b) The conclusion reassures the reader that it was all okay in the end — it rounds off the story.
c) The second paragraph moves the story along. We meet the narrators' friends, and sympathise with them too. It keeps us worried about, and interested in, what happens.

Q3 any reasonable answer

Q4 Introductory Starters: b, d, f
Concluding Starters: a, c, e

Section Four Different Types of Non-Fiction

Page 36

Q1 are, makes, (stick), (have), are, (have), have

Q2 impersonal statements: b), c), d)
personal statements: a), e)

Q3, Q4: any reasonable answer

Page 37

Q1 was, took, ran, got, chased, was, could, had, was, opened, jumped, drove

Q2 any reasonable answer

Q3 correct order: d), b), c), a)

Q4 a) during (or after)
b) as soon as (or after or while)
c) while
d) later on
e) until (or while)
f) after

Page 38

Q1 a) check, check, do, offer, check, type, are
b) any reasonable answer

Q2 impersonal statements: c), d)
personal statements: a), b)

Q3 a) so (or therefore)
b) because
c) in order that (or so)
d) therefore (or so)
e) as a result
f) then

Page 39

Q1 a) e.g. Be home before midnight.
b) e.g. Light the blue touch-paper then stand well back.
c) e.g. Hand in your homework before Friday.
d) e.g. Overpower the Dark Lord and then rescue the princess in the tower.
e) e.g. Walk the dog before you leave for school.
f) e.g. Read all the instructions before starting to glue the components together.
g) e.g. Do not press the red button.

Q2 a) Check with an adult that it is safe for you to make lunch. Open the can of beans. Empty the beans into the saucepan. Turn the cooker on. Slice the bread and put it in the toaster. Take out a plate and cutlery. Butter the toast. Pour the beans on the toast.
b) Wheel your bike out of the shed. Stand your bike in the yard. Fill a bucket half full of hot water. Put in one capful of detergent. Stir the water well with the sponge to dissolve the soap fully. Clean all the surfaces thoroughly with soapy water. Get a fresh bucket of cold water and use it to rinse the bike. Let your bike dry properly before putting it back in the shed.

Q3 any reasonable answer

Page 40

Q1 I really am sorry; I do regret; I know it was daft; I wish I could find some way to apologise; I can only promise that it will not happen again.

Q2 any reasonable answer

Q3 a) opinion — I really don't agree with foxhunting. I think it's cruel and barbaric.
reason — I think this because of the immense suffering that the innocent foxes are subjected to.
example — I heard of one hunt which took 4 1/2 hours to finish, at which point the fox was ripped to pieces by hounds.
opinion — I think it's utterly inhumane and should be stopped.

b) opinion — I think television's great
reason — because you can get more up-to-date information than you can get from books.
example — Just last night I was watching a documentary about pollution that was only filmed last month.
opinion — I disagree with people who say that telly rots the brain. I think they're just being narrow-minded.

Page 41

Q1 b) King Harold had a lot of bad luck as he raced down to face the Norman invasion. On the other hand, William the Conqueror was better organised and more determined.
c) Watching too much television stops children reading. Another point of view is that many books only become popular with young readers because they are televised.
d) School uniform is a good advertisement for the school. But you can also argue that school kids who wear raggedy ties, untucked shirts and who misbehave on the high street at lunch time only get the school a bad name.
e) If more people cycled to work all year round, there would be less pollution and so people would be healthier. However, some people would also argue that there would inevitably be a rise in accidents with cars, and some riders would be injured for life.

Q2 words to be underlined:
a) It seems to me that
b) but in my opinion
c) I really don't agree with
d) I think that

Q3 any reasonable answer

The Answers

Page 42

Q1 a) ii) b) i) c) iv) d) iii) e) v) f) vii) g) vi)

Q2 i) d) ii) f) iii) c) iv) e)

Section Five Different Varieties of English

Page 43

Q1 Formal
- a) How do you do?
- d) The department store was very crowded.
- e) I am afraid I do not know.
- g) I wonder if you could help me?

Informal
- b) Watcher, mate.
- c) There were, like, millions of people in the shop.
- e) I dunno, do I?
- h) Give us a hand.

Q2 any reasonable answer

Q3
- a) your brother — informal
- b) your head teacher — formal
- c) a visiting politician — formal
- d) your best friend — informal

Q4
- a) iii)
- b) i)
- c) ii)

Q5 any reasonable answer

Q6
- a) informal
- b) formal
- c) formal
- d) formal
- e) informal
- f) informal

Page 44

Q1
- a) The article is all about "Eng-er-land!" = It looks at patriotism.
- b) We didn't half laugh. = It amused us.
- c) The dog was down the street in a flash. = It ran very quickly.
- d) Everyone thinks it's a rubbish idea. = It was unpopular.

Q2 Any suitable answers, for example:
- a) During his lifetime, many people died young.
- b) Many people also suffered from the plague.
- c) Occasionally the theatres were closed to prevent the plague from spreading.
- d) Fortunately for him, he never caught the plague.
- e) It is believed that, as well as being a playwright, Shakespeare was an actor.

Q3
- a) gutted
- b) dumps
- c) cats and dogs
- d) get lost
- e) conked out
- f) a good old chinwag

Q4 (suggestions)
- a) very disappointed
- b) leaves
- c) very heavily
- d) go away
- e) broken down, broken
- f) a chat, a conversation

Q5 Any suitable letter, for example:

Dear Sir,

I was most disappointed by my last visit to your cinema. The visit started badly when I ordered a small popcorn and received the most ludicrously enormous bucket.

I took up my seat, only to find an appalling amount of rubbish under my seat, a considerable health and safety hazard.

When the film itself started I could barely hear because of noisy children at the front. The cinema staff did nothing to deal with this problem.

I trust you appreciate my considerable disappointment and I would like to make it clear I shall not be returning to your cinema unless a full refund is received.

Yours sincerely

Mr W. Hinger

Page 45

Q1 Older texts
- a) (from *Tess of the D'Urbervilles* by Thomas Hardy)
- d) (from *The Turn of the Screw* by Henry James)
- e) (from *Emma* by Jane Austen)

Modern Texts

b), c), f)

Q2
- a) True
- b) False
- c) True
- d) True
- e) False
- f) True

Q3 any reasonable answers — for example:
- b) "twain" = two of them or "visitation" = trouble / difficulty
- c) any reasonable modernisation — following sentences are examples:
  We sat around the fire breathless.
  The story gripped us — a strange gruesome story, perfect for Christmas Eve in an old house.
  I don't remember what was said.
  Then someone spoke. It was the first time they had heard of such a visitation coming to a child.

Section Six Research and Study Skills

Page 46

Q1
- a) specialist magazine / website
- b) encyclopedia / website
- c) dictionary / website
- d) newspaper / website
- e) dictionary / website
- f) newspaper / website
- g) thesaurus / website

Q2 d) a) f) c) e) b)

Q3 Glossary
- a) Fathom — 1.83 metres
- d) limerick — short humorous poem of five lines and regular rhyme
- f) Stage left — to the left of an actor on stage facing the audience
- h) Pula — unit of currency in Botswana

Index
- b) Winter plants and how to nourish them
- c) 1917—The Russian Revolution
- e) Drawing Still Life
- g) The Largest Countries in the World

Q4
- b) call up search engine
- d) enter 'World Cup 1998'
- f) skim through the sites until you find an official one that is in English
- a) open the website
- c) scan the home page for key words and useful links
- g) click on a hotlink to "Opening Game"
- h) scan the page for the section on the first game
- e) write down the answer: Brazil v Scotland

The Answers

Page 47

Q1 (This task usually provides fruitful discussion: this order is a suggestion) most thorough to quickest = c), d), b), a)

Q2 a) matches c) check
b) matches a) scan
c) matches b) skim
d) matches d) edit

Q3 Madeleine, and she complained the mince pies were running out

Q4 Choose three from reggae, garage, country, soft rock.

Q5 "Busses" should be 'buses'
"on" should be 'one'
"fllowing" should be 'following'

Page 48

Q1 All of them can be used to present information

Q2 a) graph
b) table
c) paragraph
d) list
e) photograph
f) sketch
g) web page
h) pie chart

Q3 The following are suggested answers:
a) Number 1) because it only mentions those in support of cutting the hours.
b) Number 3) because none of them would want to be in the minority.
c) Number 2) because it shows that only five people took part in the survey.

Page 49

Q1 True = b), c), d)

Q2 Notes needed in a), b), c), and d)

Q3 Notes = a), c), d), f)

Q4 'Good' notes = d) and e)

Page 50

Q1 a) iii)
b) iii)
c) ii)

Q2 b) i) and c) iii)

Q3 a) iii), ii), i)
b) iii), ii) [(i) is irrelevant]
c) ii), i) [(iii) is irrelevant]

Q4 a) footnote or reference
b) bibliography
c) acknowledging a quote

Q5 a) acknowledging a quote
b) footnotes or reference
c) bibliography

Page 51

Q1 a) visualising
b) predicting
c) empathising
d) relating to your own experience

Q2 a) empathising / relating to your own experience
b) empathising
c) predicting

Q3 a) John is angry
b) Martha feels guilty
c) The doctor is becoming ill too
d) She is cruel, manipulative, horrible

Q4 Key words underlined
a) "stormed" and "slammed" imply anger
b) "stared accusingly" and "shuffled uncomfortably"
c) "pale as death", "half-defeated", "tickle in his throat" and "summoning some energy" all suggest he is sick
d) "vicious" suggests a cruel streak
"*my* rules" implies she is manipulative

Page 52

Q1 a) matches iv)
b) matches iii)
c) matches ii)
d) matches i)

Q2 a) matches ii)
b) matches i) and ii)
c) matches iii)
d) matches i)

Page 53

Q1 a) matches (i)
b) matches (iii)
c) matches (ii)
d) matches (iv)

Q2 "children are safer if they have a phone to keep in touch with home"

Q3 any reasonable answers — for example:
a) It's a load of nonsense
b) He thinks it's amazing and he's very happy.
c) Very distraught and has had to quit his job.
d) The writer is detached, but seems to have an amused tone of voice. I think he or she is a little entertained by the whole thing.

Page 54

Q1 a) matches iv)
b) matches i)
c) matches ii)
d) matches iii)

Q2 "Older People" = a), b), f)
"Younger People" = c), d), e)

Q3 a) True
b) False
c) False
d) True

Q4 Young people / teenagers (both b) and c))

Q5 a) 2
b) 3
c) 3
d) 1
e) 1
f) 2

Q6 any reasonable answer

Page 55

Q1 These are suggestions:
a) romantic location, ideal for couples who want to be alone
b) fresh ingredients are used in the products
c) the insurance product leaves you nothing to worry about; also includes a protective image for customer to feel safe with
d) dog with bowl is deliberately similar to image of a person begging for money, which is what the charity wants from you

Q2 a) matches Q1 (b)
b) matches Q1 (c)
c) matches Q1 (d)
d) matches Q1 (a)

The Answers

Q3 a) suggests freshness as well as the product being natural
b) adds to meaning to suggest that not only does the product offer peace of mind, but that the company is a protective parent figure to its customers
c) these noises make the cause more difficult to ignore, and more urgent that something should be done
d) suggests the place is lively and fun, as well as having a romantic aspect

Q4 True = (a), (c), (d), (f), (g), (h)

Section Seven
Authors' Craft

Page 56

Q1 a) v)
b) iii)
c) ii)
d) iv)
e) i)

Q2 any reasonable answer

Q3 most obvious choices:
Mrs Pinchfist,
Mrs Frostymouth,
Mr Tightheart

Q4 any reasonable answers

Page 57

Q1 Shopping List:

Dairy Products:
Milk
Cheese
Cream

Meat:
Mince
Chicken breasts

Vegetables:
Potatoes
Onions
Carrots

Fruit:
Bananas
Oranges
Kiwi fruit

Toiletries:
Shampoo
Conditioner
Cotton wool

Q2 a) your address
the number of the bus
the time of the bus
a description of the bag
the contents of the bag
your contact phone number
b) any reasonable answer

Q3 a) any reasonable answers, e.g.
G, H, E, F, A, B, D, C
b) any reasonable answer

Page 58

Q1 a) am not, is not etc...
b) that is not possible
c) going to
d) please wait
e) I understand
f) thank you

Q2 any reasonable answer

Q3 a) Bang! She slammed the door shut, and stormed off down the corridor, her heels clicking on the hard floor.
Crash! The sound of crockery hitting the kitchen floor made him jump, as did the clattering of the cutlery following it.
b) any reasonable answer

Q4 any reasonable answer

Page 59

Q1 a) when somebody suddenly remembers a past event
b) looking backwards in time
c) a book where you write your actions and thoughts
d) the person telling the story
e) the story

Q2 most likely answer:
B: He saw someone from the past

Q3 any reasonable answer

Q4 a) any reasonable answer, e.g. it helps the reader to follow the story, the reader knows exactly what order everything happens.
b) any reasonable answer, e.g. it helps to create suspense or mystery by starting with an unexplained event.
c) any interesting order, e.g.
Man wakes up on Jupiter.
[flashback]
Man goes into pub.
Man is walking home.
Man sees bright light.
Aliens kidnap man.

Page 60

Q1 a) i) The victorious warrior queen rode triumphantly into the town.
ii) The cheating warrior queen rode shamefully into the town.
b) any reasonable answer

Q2 a) Anna (shouting) *Where have you been? It's past midnight!*
Bobby (sulkily) *Nowhere.*
Anna (angrily) *What do you mean, nowhere?*
Bobby (loudly) *I was just out.*
Anna (slamming down her book) *Tell me the truth!*
b) any reasonable answer

Q3 a) best answer is A
b) best answer is B

Section Eight
Literary Texts

Page 61

Q1 any reasonable answer

Q2 any reasonable answer

Q3 any reasonable answer

Q4 a) The protagonist is the central character that the action is based around. This person often drives the plot forward and makes events happen — usually the goodie.
b) The antagonist is a character who is opposite to the central character who makes things happen — usually the baddie.

Q5 any reasonable answer

Q6 any reasonable answer

Q7 any reasonable answer

Page 62

Q1 a) the playwright
b) the director
c) the actors
d) the prompt
e) backstage hands
f) the audience

Q2 a) iii)
b) ii)
c) v)
d) iv)
e) i)
f) vi)

The Answers

Q3 a) iii)
b) i)
c) ii)

Q4 e)

Page 63

Q1 brain/insane and gentle/mental

Q2 any reasonable answer

Q3 b) fourteen

Q4 c), because lines 2 and 4 rhyme, and it has a very regular rhythm. Also, it's the most storyish one.

Q5 a) 5, b) 7 and c) 5

Page 64

Q1 a) iv)
b) ii)
c) iii)
d) i)

Q2 a)

Q3 a)

Q4 c)

Q5 any reasonable answer

Section Nine
Essay Skills

Page 65

Q1 a) plan — plan, planner
b) draft — draft
c) edit — edition, editor
d) proofread — proofreader
e) write — writer, writing

Q2 any reasonable answer

Q3 a) journal
b) mental mapping
c) brainstorming

Q4 any reasonable answer

Q5 any reasonable answer

Q6 any reasonable answer

Q7 any reasonable answer

Page 66

Q1 any reasonable answers

Q2 any reasonable answer

Q3 any reasonable answers

Q4 any reasonable answers — for example:
It should all be in the same font.
Text should be all upper case or lower case, and in the same style (e.g. italic).
The name and speech should be separated by the same character in each case (e.g. colon).
Correct spacing should be used, e.g. one space at the end of a word, two spaces after a full stop.

Section Ten
Writing Fiction

Page 67

Q1 a) ii)
b) iv)
c) iii)
d) v)
e) i)

Q2 any reasonable answer

Q3 a), b) and c) are all true and d) is false.

Q4 She screams because she's frightened of what scraped her cheek.

Q5 any reasonable answer

Page 68

Q1 grumpy (or grumpily)

Q2 a) direct action — In fact, that very morning, grumpily, Roy thumped the television with his fist.
b) direct description — Roy was a grumpy man, no doubt about it.
c) direct dialogue — 'Roy is one seriously grumpy man!' Steve said.

Q3 a) indirect description — He never smiled at his neighbours or said a friendly hello.
b) indirect dialogue — 'Yeah he even growls at the checkout girl,' added Katie.
c) indirect action — When his dog tried to wag at other dogs in the park, Roy always roughly dragged him away.

Q4 any reasonable answer

Page 69

Q1 'something'

Q2 any reasonable answer e.g. 'What is the something that is rustling in the darkness?'

Q3 a)

Q4 a)

Q5 any reasonable answers

Page 70

Q1 a) and iii)
b) and i)
c) and v)
d) and ii)
e) and iv)

Q2 a)
i) She heard the pitter-patter of little feet scurrying across the mooden floor.
ii) The water dripped slowly over the stones.
iii) There was a steady bang-bang-bang from the drum.
iv) The rustle of leaves underfoot is a sure sign that autumn's here.
v) Her feet were neat and petite.
vi) He could hear the chink of teacups on the lawn.
vii) I've seen the sun on the silver sand.

b)
i) Short (quick) vowel sounds match the quick movement.
ii) Long (slow) vowel sounds match the slow action.
iii) The rhythmic sound matches the thing being described.
iv) The added word sounds like the thing it describes.
v) Word endings rhyme.
vi) The added word sounds like the thing it describes.
vii) The same sound occurs at the start of several words.

Q3 a) The boiling broth bubbled on the bonfire.
b) Wet, weary, and worried, the wanderers returned.
c) She wore shiny shoes and a shimmering shawl.
d) the sound of the hissing and steaming stream
e) It was delicious and nutritious.

Q4 any reasonable answer

The Answers

Section Eleven
Writing Information

Page 71

Q1 b) There were only seconds left to act, which caused me to panic and lose control.
c) I had completed my labours for the day, so I put my feet up and relaxed.
d) It was blowing an absolute gale, so my granny hung her knickers out to dry.

Q2, Q3: any reasonable answers

Page 72

Q1, Q3, Q4: any reasonable answers

Q2 b), d), e)

Page 73

Q1, Q2: any reasonable answers

Q3 a) Get dressed, have some breakfast, brush your teeth and walk to school.
b) Put your seatbelt on, start your engine, indicate to move out and accelerate.
c) Have your immunisation shots, fly to Morocco, put sun tan lotion on and buy some souvenirs.
d) Cross the road, get run over, lie still on the ground and call an ambulance.
e) Have your main meal, watch some television, get undressed and go to bed.
f) Open the tin of food, put the food in a bowl and give the bowl to the dog.
g) Put on your boots, kick the football, score a goal and do a little dance.

Page 74

All questions: any reasonable answer

Section Twelve
Writing To Persuade

Page 75

Q1 any reasonable answer

Q2 In the right situation, the following could be used as rhetorical questions: b), c), e), g), j), k), m), n), o)

Q3 any reasonable answer

Page 76

Q1 a) to d) any reasonable answers. Examples may include Government websites, Guiness Book of Records, Channel 4 Information, and MacDonalds Company Information or other statistical websites.

Q2 a) bad
b) good
c) good
d) good
e) bads

Q3, Q4: any reasonable answer

Page 77

Q1: any reasonable answer

Q2 d) because it insults the intended reader and will put them off

Q3 You'll have to ask your teacher for the answers to these.

Section Thirteen
Critical Writing

Page 78

Q1 Good points
A monkey smiled at me.
I was allowed to feed the seals.
I was allowed to stroke lots of cute piglets.
I ate ice-cream.

Bad points
The lions escaped and ate my uncle.
The elephants still have my wallet.
The boa constricter ate one of the meerkats.
I dropped my camera into the penguin pool.

Q2, Q3, Q4: any reasonable answers

Page 79

Q1, Q2: any reasonable answers

Q3 a) no b) yes c) no d) yes e) yes